CLIMATE, THE ENVIRONMENT AND PEOPLE

HEINEMANN GEOGRAPHY
for
AVERY HILL

1

Gary Cambers  *Currie*

Heinemann Educational Publishers
Halley Court, Jordan Hill, Oxford OX2 8EJ
a division of Reed Educational & Professional Publishing Ltd

OXFORD FLORENCE PRAGUE MADRID ATHENS
MELBOURNE AUCKLAND KUALA LUMPUR SINGAPORE TOKYO
IBADAN NAIROBI KAMPALA JOHANNESBURG GABORONE
PORTSMOUTH NH (USA) CHICAGO MEXICO CITY SAO PAOLO

Text © Gary Cambers, Stuart Currie

First published 1997

00 99 98 97
10 9 8 7 6 5 4 3 2 1

British Library Cataloguing in Publication Data
A catalogue record for this book is available from the British Library

ISBN 0 435 34107 3

Typeset and designed by The Wooden Ark, Leeds
Printed and bound in Spain by Mateu Cromo

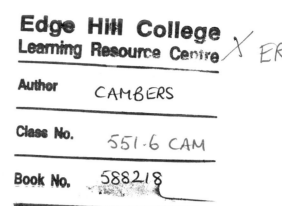
Acknowledgements

The publishers would like to thank the following for permission to reproduce copyright material.

Maps and extracts

24 Hour Famine, advert in *Shout Magazine* for 1994 24 Hour Famine (p. 34A); Crystal Holidays (p. 9E); Explore Worldwide (pp. 9G, 15D); *FARM-Africa*, Summer 1996 (p.35F); Geographical Association (p. 52 logo); *Geographical Magazine*, January 1994 (p. 15E), April 1994 (p. 42B), October 1995 (p. 23E); Greenpeace UK (p. 62 logo); reproduced from data supplied by The Met. Office; Ordnance Survey © Crown Copyright (p.52A right); RSPB (p. 62 logo); *The Observer*, 22 November 1987 (p. 20A); Michael Palin, *Pole to Pole* (BBC Books) (p. 57D); *The Times* 21 September, 1992 (p. 25F), 12 December 1996 (p. 41F); Thomson Holidays (pp.8, 15D); L Williams, *Understanding the Polar Lands*, (Evans Brothers Ltd) (p. 25D); World Wide Fund for Nature © 1986 (p. 62 logo).

Photographs

Abercrombie & Kent Travel (p. 25E); Action Plus/D Davies (p. 17 E); AirFotos Ltd (p. 47E); Heather Angel (p. 45B); Associated Press (p. 61C); Aviemore Photographic (p. 7A left); BBC (p. 7D); Bridgeman Art Library/Museum of London (p. 26A); Bruce Coleman/E Chrichton (p. 30B); Bryan and Cherry Alexander (p. 42A); Gary Cambers (p. 6A right); Stuart Currie (pp. 28B, 37C both, 57 top right, bottom left); Cambridgeshire County Council (p. 17C); Collections/Dorothy Burrows (p. 6A left), John & Eliza Forder (p. 7A right), Select (p. 20B top); Colorific (p. 32A right); Dundee University (p. 21D); Environmental Images (p. 56A); Environmental Picture Library (p. 62 right); FARM-Africa (p. 35E, F); Frank Lane Picture Agency (p. 48A); Greenpeace/Morgan (p. 53); Guardian Newspapers (p. 62 left); Mary Evans Picture Library (p. 36A); NHPA/ R Tidman (p. 18A); Nottingham Evening Post (p. 16A); Panos Pictures/S Sprague (p. 12A bottom right), D Harcourt-Webster (p. 30A3), J Morris (p. 32A left), B Paton (p. 32A middle), B Press (p. 35D), H Bradner (p. 43C); Planet Earth/M Ogilvie (p. 41D); Popperfoto/Reuters (pp. 11E, 20B bottom, 24C, 42 right,); Press Association (p. 59 top); Robert Harding Picture Library (pp. 5, 12A left, 24A, 54B); Science Photo Library/NASA (pp. 4, 37D, 49D), NOAA (p. 22A), NRSC (p. 33D), T Van Sant/Geosphere Project (p. 40A); Scotsman Publications Ltd (p. 27E); Spectrum Colour Library (p. 9G); T Starkey (p. 34B); Still Pictures/C Martin (p. 12A top right), L Murray (p. 30A4), R Seitre (p. 30A1), F Hoogervorst (p. 29), Klein/Hubert (p. 30A2), N Dickinson (pp. 38A, 39D), M Edwards (p. 50B), D Hoffman (p. 59 bottom); Trip Photo Library/ M Feeney (p. 8D), T Fisher (p. 15D), H Rogers (p. 15E); Zefa (p. 57D bottom right).

The publishers have made every effort to trace the copyright holders, but if they have inadvertently overlooked any, they will be pleased to make the necessary arrangements at the first opportunity.

Contents

Location of case studies

1 **Weather and climate**

- UK – London, Glasgow
- Spain – Costa Blanca, Benidorm
- Italy – Cortina, Sicily, Piedmont
- India – Damodara
- Australia – Wyndham
- USA – Florida
- Antarctica

2 **Natural environments**

- Russia
- Borneo
- Ethiopia
- Italy – Po Delta
- Africa – Sahel zone
- UK – Midlands, North-East
- Mediterranean

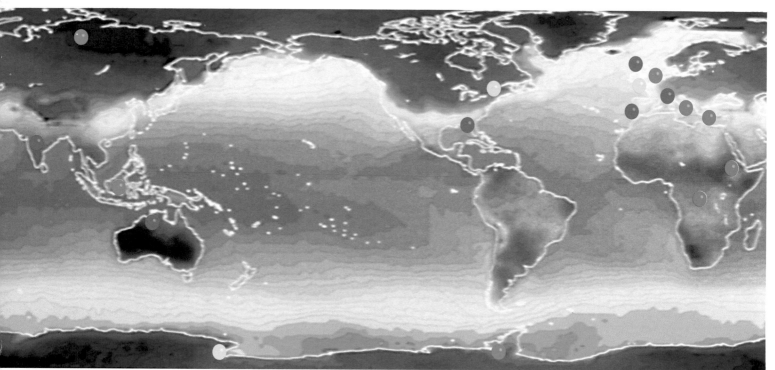

Satellite image of the world, showing world temperature bands

3 **Issues of global concern**

- Antarctica
- USA – Adirondacks
- UK
- World – deltas and small islands, eg. Pacific groups.

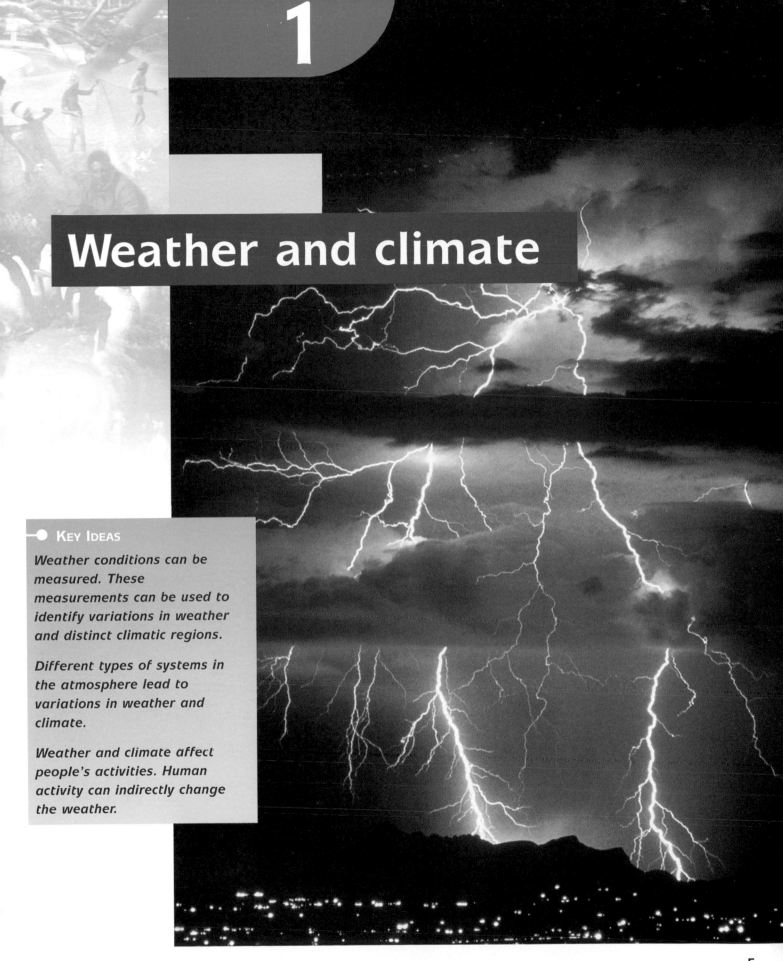

1

Weather and climate

KEY IDEAS

Weather conditions can be measured. These measurements can be used to identify variations in weather and distinct climatic regions.

Different types of systems in the atmosphere lead to variations in weather and climate.

Weather and climate affect people's activities. Human activity can indirectly change the weather.

1.1 It depends on the weather

A These four photos show how weather affects our daily lives

Rain, sunshine, wind or snow?

What is the **weather** like today? Has it changed since you came to school? The weather in the UK is very variable. We are interested in the weather because so many of our day to day activities and jobs depend on it. We cannot, however, always rely on the weather.

B The weather influences many jobs

1 Look at the photos in **Source A**.
a Which positive aspects of weather conditions are shown?
b How has the weather created difficulties for people?
c What do you understand by 'good weather' and 'bad weather'?

2 **Source B** shows some of the jobs in the UK which can be affected by different types of weather.
a Explain how the weather would affect four of the jobs in the illustration.
b Compare your ideas with others in your class.
c Explain why some jobs are not affected by the weather.

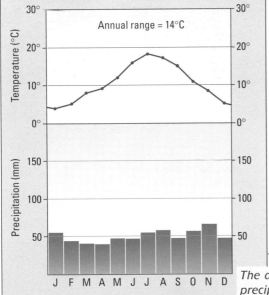

Annual range = 14°C

Temperature (°C)

Precipitation (mm)

J F M A M J J A S O N D

 C

The average temperature and precipitation for London are shown on this climate graph

Weather and climate

When variations in daily weather conditions are averaged out over a number of years, the pattern describes a country's **climate**.

In the UK temperatures are neither too hot nor too cold. Such a climate with no extremes is called **temperate**. This is due to its location between the cold, arctic region (north of $66\frac{1}{2}°N$) and the hot Tropic of Cancer ($23\frac{1}{2}°N$). Being close to the Atlantic Ocean, the UK receives prevailing winds from the south-west which bring rain all year round. The UK has what is known as a cool temperate **maritime** climate.

D *The weather refers to the changes which take place day to day*

Tomorrow will have sunshine and cloud in the south, becoming cloudier and cooler in the north. Northern and western areas will receive blizzards but in the east the snow may turn to rain. A top temperature of 7°C in the south but only reaching -2°C in Scotland. So wrap up warm!

	J	F	M	A	M	J	J	A	S	O	N	D
Temperature (°C)	4	5	7	9	12	16	18	17	15	11	8	5
Precipitation (mm)	54	40	37	37	46	45	57	59	49	57	64	48

Total precipitation = 593mm

3 Study the climate graph in **Source C**.
   a Use an atlas to describe the location of London. Include its latitude and longitude.
   b Use the graph to help you describe London's climate. Refer to:
      (i) maximum and minimum temperature
      (ii) annual temperature range
      (iii) precipitation total
      (iv) precipitation distribution.

4 Explain the difference between weather and climate.

5 Find a weather forecast for tomorrow. How does it compare to the forecast in **Source D**? Comment on the similarities and differences.

GALES

Blizzards

Windy

Overnight
frost & fog

1.2

Due south!

How do the weather and climate in the Mediterranean differ from that in the UK?

Why does the Mediterranean attract tourists from the UK?

Which types of Mediterranean holiday depend on the weather and climate?

Mediterranean holidays

Today many UK residents travel to other countries for their main holiday. Great numbers travel south during the peak holiday months of July and August to the islands and resorts of the Mediterranean.

The Costa Blanca, or 'white coast', of Spain is due south from London. The popularity of resorts like Benidorm has lasted for over 20 years.

Maximum daily temperatures forecast for 28 July 1996

A

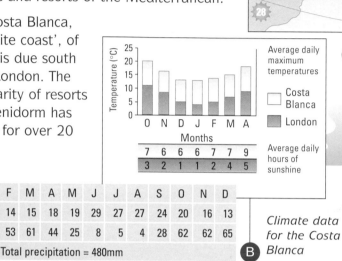

Climate data for the Costa Blanca

B

	J	F	M	A	M	J	J	A	S	O	N	D
Temperature (°C)	13	14	15	18	19	29	27	27	24	20	16	13
Precipitation (mm)	63	53	61	44	25	8	5	4	28	62	62	65

Total precipitation = 480mm

Top ten summer destinations 1996 (UK visitors only)

C

Fact file ...   Benidorm: fact or fiction?

Location: Benidorm stands above two beaches of soft, pale sand about 50km from Alicante.
Beaches: Long sandy beaches regarded as the cleanest and safest in the Mediterranean.
Sports: Bowling is very popular or tee off on one of the area's three golf courses.

Night-life: Appealing to every taste and budget. Home comforts include roast dinners and fish and chips or Spanish fare if you fancy a change.
Plus points: Superb sandy beaches and a resort dedicated to holiday entertainment.
Finally: Hunt for bargains in the many fascinating shops of the Old Town.

Source: Thomson Holidays

1 Study **Source A**.
  a What temperatures are forecast for Majorca and Tenerife in July?
  b Look at the climate graph for London on page 7. Explain why the Mediterranean region has so many visitors from the UK in summer.

2 Study **Source B**. To what extent are UK travel agents justified in using the slogan 'Come to Benidorm for your winter break!'?

3 a Using the map in **Source D** and an atlas, describe Benidorm's location.
  b From which direction was the photo in **Source D** taken?
  c How does Benidorm compare with your image or experience of a British seaside resort?
  d What disadvantages might the popularity of Benidorm have for the local people and the environment?

4 Design a poster to advertise the advantages of a summer holiday in Benidorm for travellers from the UK.

D

From Italian ski slopes...

The climate is not always hot and dry in the Mediterranean region. In countries like Italy, the climate can vary a great deal. Those land masses which are further from the influence of the sea experience a wider range of temperatures. They heat up and cool down more than coastal areas. This pattern is called **continentality**. In mountainous areas like the Italian Alps, winter temperatures can be very low – good news for skiers!

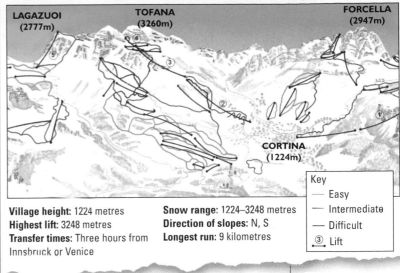

Cortina has excellent facilities for all types of skier and scored higher than any other in *The Daily Mail Ski Magazine's* extensive survey. Cortina is the 'Queen of the Alps' with its unrivalled setting in the Dolomites offering the best skiing in Italy if altitude and run lengths count.

Cortina

LAGAZUOI (2777m)   TOFANA (3260m)   FORCELLA (2947m)

CORTINA (1224m)

Village height: 1224 metres
Highest lift: 3248 metres
Transfer times: Three hours from Innsbruck or Venice

Snow range: 1224–3248 metres
Direction of slopes: N, S
Longest run: 9 kilometres

Key
— Easy
— Intermediate
— Difficult
③ → Lift

Source: Crystal Holidays

E   *Cortina, Queen of the Alps*

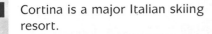

Relief photo of Italy (excluding Sardinia)

Cortina

Milan

Venice

45°N

F

N

0   100   200km

Rome

Brindisi

Naples
Mt Vesuvius
40°N

Mt Stromboli

Palermo

Mt Etna

5   Cortina is a major Italian skiing resort.
    a   Use **Sources E** and **F** to describe its location. Refer to altitude, latitude and distance from the sea in your answer.
    b   Imagine you are going to ski to Cortina from one of the three highest points. Begin at Lagazuoi, Tofana or Forcella. Choose and describe your route.
    c   How and why might temperatures change as you ski down the mountains?

6   Study the information from the travel brochure in **Source G**. Suggest why Explore Worldwide does not organize visits from:
    a   November to April
    b   mid-July to August.

7   **a**   You have now studied Mediterranean holidays in Benidorm, Cortina and Sicily. Briefly describe the holiday you would prefer.
    b   Explain how weather and climate influenced your decision.

...to Sicilian sun strokes!

Travel firms only organize their holidays when they expect to make a profit. Explore Worldwide offers adventure holidays in small groups to more challenging areas of the world. The weather and season affect not only the price that can be charged for holidays but also when certain places can be visited in comfort.

April–May and October–November are pleasantly warm. June–September are the hottest months. Due to the altitude nights may be cold on Mt Etna, and snow may still be seen on the summit in April. Late November onwards can be rainy.

G   *Backpacking on Mt Etna*

Italy

SICILIAN VOLCANO HIKE

8 days from LONDON start Sat end Sat

1997	Price in £		Price in £
10 May–17 May	639	13 Sep–20 Sep	649
24 May–31 May	639	20 Sep–27 Sep	649
07 Jun–14 Jun	639	04 Oct–11 Oct	649
21 Jun–28 Jun	639	11 Oct–18 Oct	649
05 Jul–12 Jul	639	18 Oct–25 Oct	649
06 Sep–13 Sep	649		

Source: Explore Worldwide

Palermo average day temperatures												
	J	F	M	A	M	J	J	A	S	O	N	D
Temperature (°C)	16	16	17	20	24	27	30	30	28	25	21	18

1.3 Flooding in Piedmont, Italy

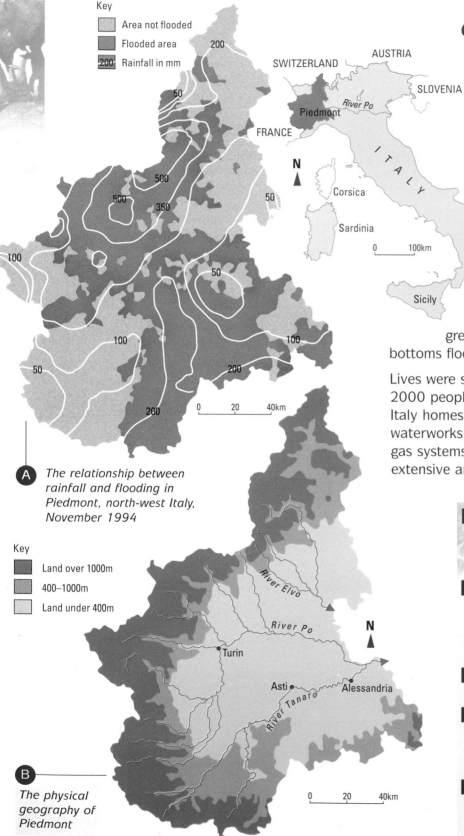

Key
- Area not flooded
- Flooded area
- 200 Rainfall in mm

A The relationship between rainfall and flooding in Piedmont, north-west Italy, November 1994

Key
- Land over 1000m
- 400–1000m
- Land under 400m

B The physical geography of Piedmont

Causes and effects

In early November 1994 a period of heavy rain hit north-west Italy. Widespread flooding followed. The Italian districts of Liguria, Lombardy and Piedmont were severely affected as well as parts of Spain, Morocco and southern France. About 65 people died because of the floods.

Within Piedmont the effects of the flooding varied according to the height, or altitude, of an area. In mountainous areas there was little damage because, as time went on, snow rather than rain fell at lower levels. In hilly areas and in the mountain foothills the rapid flow of water caused a great deal of erosion. In flat areas and valley bottoms flooding was widespread over very large areas.

Lives were seriously disrupted. In Asti, for example, 2000 people were evacuated. Throughout north-west Italy homes, crops, buildings, bridges, factories, roads, waterworks, sewers, the electricity grid, telephone and gas systems were all badly affected. The damage was extensive and costs were estimated at £2.5 billion.

1
a Which areas of Italy were affected by the flooding?
b Using **Source A** and an atlas, describe the location of Piedmont.

2 Use **Source A** to:
a describe the extent of the flooded area in Piedmont
b compare the rainfall patterns with the extent of the flooded area.

3 How does **Source B** help to explain the relationship between rainfall and flooding?

4 Use **Source C** to describe:
a the location of high and low pressure centres over Europe
b how this affects wind direction.

5 Use **Sources C** and **D** to explain how the position of high and low pressure centres caused the rainfall over Piedmont.

C *Synoptic chart for 0000 hours, 4 November 1994. The situation changed very little over the next few days. It brought a 'conveyor belt' of warm, moist air into the Piedmont district for nearly three days.*

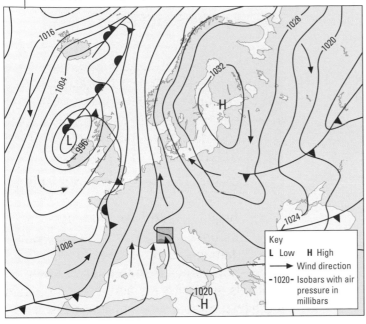

Key
L Low   H High
→ Wind direction
-1020- Isobars with air pressure in millibars

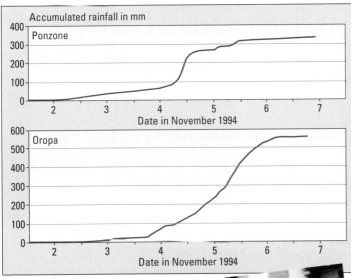

Accumulated rainfall in mm

Ponzone

Date in November 1994

Oropa

Date in November 1994

D ***Accumulated rainfall** graphs for two automatic weather stations in Piedmont – huge amounts of rain fell in just seven days*

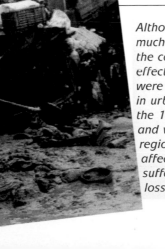

E *Although there was much damage in the countryside, the effects of the floods were most obvious in urban areas. Of the 1209 towns and villages in the region, 760 were affected and 192 suffered serious loss and damage*

Responding to the flood danger

F

Diary of the flood, November 1994

3 November	Alarm bulletins sent by weather centre to the emergency authorities. Accurate weather forecasts predicted up to 600mm of rainfall between 4 and 6 November.
4 November	Second alarm bulletin sent to the emergency authorities. Press reports of a delay in the intervention by these authorities.
6 November	First intervention by the emergency authorities.
7 November	Newspapers report two metres of water flooding Asti, Alessandria and a number of other places.
18 November	Emergency authorities still working with the army, voluntary helpers and the government to restore life to normal.

G ## After the flood period:

*   Collections were made by the press to raise money for reconstruction work.

*   The Central Government declared an emergency and approved financial assistance for the worst hit areas.

*   A major factor contributing to the flooding was the lack of dredging of the river bank.

*   It was suggested that a better river management policy was needed and that buildings should be reconstructed further away from the rivers.

6 Using information on these pages describe:
a the immediate effects of the flooding
b what longer term effects the flooding might have on the area.

7 Evaluate how the different groups mentioned in **Sources F** and **G** responded to the flood danger.

1.4 Droughts and downpours

A land which is either flooded or parched, most of India has a monsoon climate with distinct wet and dry seasons

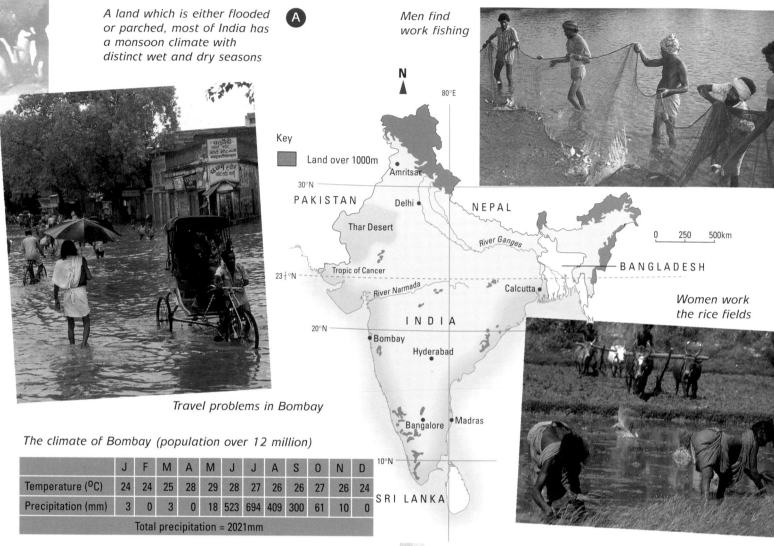

A

Men find work fishing

Travel problems in Bombay

Women work the rice fields

Key

▨ Land over 1000m

The climate of Bombay (population over 12 million)

	J	F	M	A	M	J	J	A	S	O	N	D
Temperature (°C)	24	24	25	28	29	28	27	26	26	27	26	24
Precipitation (mm)	3	0	3	0	18	523	694	409	300	61	10	0
Total precipitation = 2021mm												

Summer in the city

The **monsoon** is a seasonal wind. In the summer it blows northwards over India and Bangladesh bringing wet weather. In the winter it blows southwards over these countries towards northern Australia. This causes dry weather conditions in Bombay. These winds give distinct wet and dry seasons.

When the rains come, rivers flood the land and fish spawn in the rice fields. People put away their ploughs and get out their fishing nets as fields turn into huge lakes. In Bombay, nearly 2000mm of rain falls in the summer but very little falls at any other time. Further inland, away from the sea, temperatures are higher and there is less rain. The north-west is a particularly **arid** region.

1 Look at **Source A**.
 a What problems do the summer monsoon rains bring?
 b What opportunities for work are created by the monsoon rains?

2 a Use **Source A** to draw a climate graph for Bombay. Use the same scale as for the climate graph of London on page 7.
 b How might the location of Bombay explain the temperature figures?
 c Describe the seasonal distribution of rain in Bombay.
 d What evidence is there that some areas of India do not receive much rainfall from the monsoon?
 e Suggest how the hot, dry season would affect people's activities in and around Bombay.

B
India and the position of the Sun in June and December

Making the monsoon

Source **B** shows the position of the Earth and the Sun in June and December. **Radiation** from the Sun travels through the atmosphere and heats the ground. The ground then sends out radiation which heats the air above.

High temperatures occur where the Sun's rays heat the ground at right angles. This concentrates heat in a small area. Away from the Equator and Tropics, the Sun's rays heat the ground at shallower angles. This causes the heat to be spread over a larger area so temperatures are lower towards the polar regions.

C *Wet monsoon winds blow into India in June and dry monsoon winds blow out towards Australia in December*

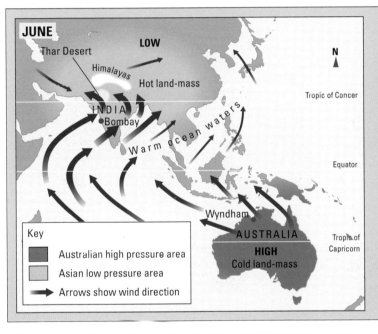

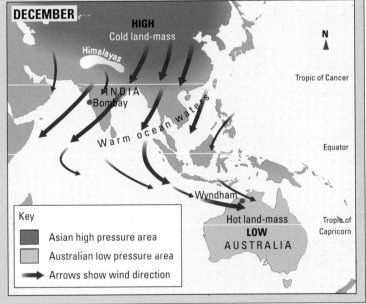

3 Look at **Source B**.
  a In which month and season will northern India and the Himalayan areas be at their hottest?
  b When will these areas be at their coolest?
  c Explain why there is a difference.

4 Study the maps in **Source C**.
  a Copy the information for June and December onto outline maps of south-east Asia and Australia.
  b From which direction do the winds blow towards India in June? Why would this be?
  c From which direction do the winds blow over India in December? Explain why.

5 Use these maps and your climate graph to describe and explain the pattern of rainfall in Bombay.

6 Study the climate data given in **Source D** for Wyndham, a small town on the north coast of Australia.
  a Compare the climates of Wyndham and Bombay.
  b Suggest why people are more aware of the monsoon season in India than in Wyndham.

D *Climate data for Wyndham, Australia (population 1500)*

	J	F	M	A	M	J	J	A	S	O	N	D
Temperature (°C)	31	30	29	29	27	24	24	25	26	29	32	31
Precipitation (mm)	254	175	110	19	6	3	0	0	3	10	28	104
Total precipitation = 712mm												

1.5 Working in a dry land

How does the monsoon system affect farming in north-west India?

How are people in north-west India using the monsoon system to change their way of life?

A nation of villages

More than 900 million people live in India. As 70 per cent of its people live in the 600 000 villages on flat plains, plateaus and mountains, the country has been called a 'nation of villages'. Most people work the land in order to live. The farming year is planned around the monsoon rains.

Damodara is a typical village in the Jaisalmer district of north-west India. It is made up of 58 households and 256 people. A recent census described the area as 'one of the most backward in the state of Rajasthan'.

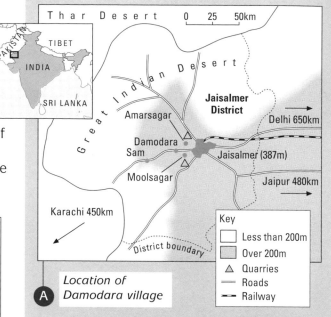

A Location of Damodara village

This community has no electricity supply nor any telephones. There is drinking water but most wells and tanks are used for livestock. It has a primary school – an empty shell buried in the sand. The nearest chemist is 20km away but there is a limited bus and postal service.

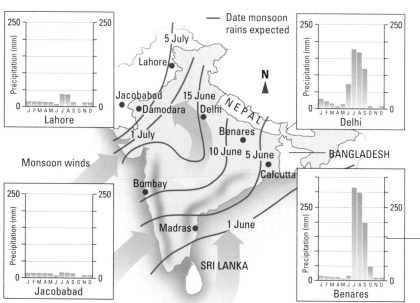

B Waiting for a wet season – the advance of the summer monsoon over India

C Working with a mini-monsoon

1 Study **Source A**.
   a Describe the location of Damodara.
   b Is this community remote? Give reasons for your opinion.

2 Look at **Source B**.
   a Describe what happens to patterns of precipitation as the winds blow north-west across India. Suggest reasons for this pattern.
   b When do the monsoon rains arrive at Damodara?

3 Refer to **Source C**.
   a How does the monsoon in the Jaisalmer district compare to Bombay's?
   b What problems does this cause farmers in Damodara?
   c What other problems do farmers have to cope with to survive here?

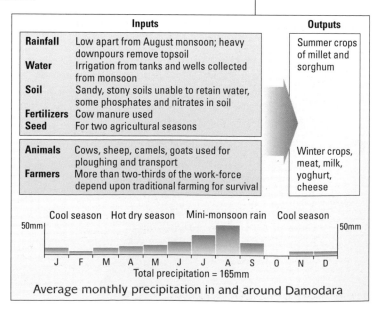

Inputs		Outputs
Rainfall	Low apart from August monsoon; heavy downpours remove topsoil	Summer crops of millet and sorghum
Water	Irrigation from tanks and wells collected from monsoon	
Soil	Sandy, stony soils unable to retain water, some phosphates and nitrates in soil	
Fertilizers	Cow manure used	
Seed	For two agricultural seasons	
Animals	Cows, sheep, camels, goats used for ploughing and transport	Winter crops, meat, milk, yoghurt, cheese
Farmers	More than two-thirds of the work-force depend upon traditional farming for survival	

Total precipitation = 165mm

Average monthly precipitation in and around Damodara

Alternatives to farming

Farming the land in such a difficult environment is hard work. A farmer's success depends on skill in managing the unpredictable water supply. This type of **subsistence** economy barely allows a community to survive on a day-to-day basis. It is no surprise that many farmers today are looking for other forms of employment.

India is now on the tourist trail of visitors from the **MEDC**s (More Economically Developed Countries) of Europe, the USA and Japan. Areas like Rajasthan have a culture and climate which interests tourists. For the villagers of Damodara, tourism offers a higher, more reliable income and a better standard of living. It allows them to buy food rather than struggle to grow it. Many farmers now have an alternative source of income.

D *Camels carry tourists to Jaisalmer Fort*

Source: Explore Worldwide

Rajasthan desert safari

22 days from LONDON

1997		1998	
start Sat end Sat	Price in £	start Sat end Sat	Price in £
04 Jan–25 Jan	1330	03 Jan–24 Jan	1330
25 Jan–15 Feb	1295	31 Jan–21 Feb	1295
08 Mar–28 Mar	1295	21 Feb–14 Mar	1295
25 Oct–15 Nov*	1330		
01 Nov–22 Nov*	1330	*visits to Pushkar camel fair	
13 Dec–03 Jan	1295		
20 Dec–10 Jan	1365		

Jaisalmer district

E

T he growing number of hotels, restaurants, and tourist shops show the growing importance of tourism. The daily jeep and camel safaris into the desert to visit remote villages like Damodara and the Sam sand dunes spread the impact further. These tourist dollars are underpinned by informal services such as foreign exchange dealing and shoe cleaning. Large numbers of people now supply food for tourists and locally-made craft goods and textiles to shops. Damodara's location on the highway linking Jaisalmer to the Sam sand dunes brings the chance to sell goods to passing tourists and to offer a quick camel trek into the desert.

Damodara finds a better way?

Source: Geographical Magazine, January 1994

Visit Pushkar camel fair and the Palaces of Rajasthan

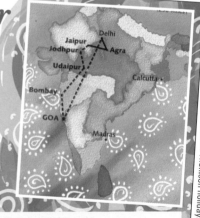

Source: Thomson holidays

4 a Using the information in **Source D** and on the previous page, design a tourist leaflet for the Jaisalmer district of India. Include a map to show its location.
 b Suggest why the Rajasthan region is on the tourist trail of people from MEDCs.

5 Study **Source E**. How might these developments affect the quality of life for the people of Damodara and Jaisalmer district?

6 'The monsoon climate and scenery of Damodara is more suited to developing tourism than farming.' To what extent would you agree with this statement? Explain your answer.

1.6 Cold as ice

Winter anticyclones

Cold **anticyclones** affect Europe in winter. They are caused by the cooling of the Earth. As the Sun is now overhead in the southern hemisphere it gives little heat to the land area of western Europe. As the land cools it chills the air above it. This sinks, causing high pressure at the Earth's surface. There are clear skies both day and night and extremely cold temperatures.

Although such subsidence of cold air only affects a layer within 2km of the ground, it has brought some of the coldest weather ever experienced in the UK.

A

Fog – another feature of winter anticyclones

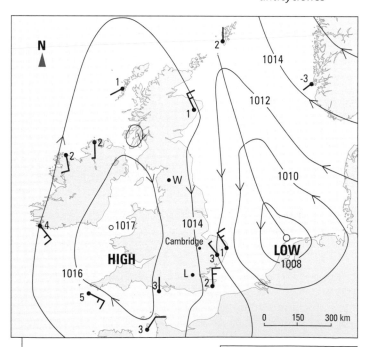

Synoptic chart of the weather conditions at 1400 hrs GMT on 12 February 1895

B

Key

—1016— Isobars: pressure in millibars

Wind direction
Wind speed:
full feather = 10 knots
half feather = 5 knots

5 Temperature °C

Poor weather stops play

The cameras at the City Ground Nottingham, for the FA Cup match between Forest and Crystal Palace couldn't even cut through the gloom. This match in January 1991, was called off before the ball could be kicked. Football has a long history of problems resulting from the effects of winter anticyclones. Frozen pitches also feature high on the list of conditions which have badly affected the sport.

The difficulties do not just affect the players. Many fans have travelled upwards of a couple of hundred kilometres only to be told that the match has been postponed and that they have no option but to return home. They have already braved icy roads and foggy conditions themselves in order to make their journey.

1 a Describe the weather conditions brought by a winter anticyclone.
  b Explain how a winter anticyclone forms.
  c Using **Source A**, describe some of the effects of a winter anticyclone on sporting events.

2 Using **Source B**, describe the anticyclone in terms of:
  • location
  • temperatures
  • wind speed and direction
  • air pressure.

A women's speed skating match in the Fens in 1895. It probably took place at Littleport in Cambridgeshire. Here 'several races were arranged one day on a special course, the prizes being a feather boa, a muff and tippet, a pair of skates and some new half crowns'

The ice on the Serpentine, Hyde Park (London) was $2\frac{1}{2}$ inches thick on Tuesday and fast approaching the skating fitness of 3 inches.
The Times, Thursday 7 February 1895

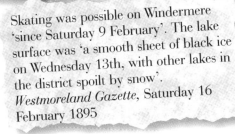

Skating was possible on Windermere 'since Saturday 9 February'. The lake surface was 'a smooth sheet of black ice on Wednesday 13th, with other lakes in the district spoilt by snow'.
Westmoreland Gazette, Saturday 16 February 1895

Diurnal (daily) **maximum and minimum temperatures** *at the Cambridge Observatory. There were air frosts at Cambridge on 70 out of 84 nights between 26 December 1894 and 20 March 1895. With clear skies and, because of the season, a weak sun, heating during the day was slow. Heat loss at night was rapid*

3 Describe the location of Cambridge in relation to the centre of the anticyclone.

4 a Study **Source C**. Describe the skating opportunities offered in terms of their geographical extent, ice requirements and the activities.

b Compare these with the activities and environment shown in **Source E**.

5 Study **Source D**.

a What is meant by the diurnal range of temperature?

b When were the largest and smallest diurnal ranges of temperature recorded at Cambridge?

c Describe the trend shown on the graph.

d Explain the patterns shown by the graph.

6 Discuss the hypothesis that 'People's leisure activities are no longer controlled by the weather'.

Leisure ice skating at Gillingham

1.7 Hot and bothered

How does a summer anticyclone form and develop?

What effect do summer anticyclones have on people?

Summer anticyclones

Early August 1990 brought some of the hottest conditions England has ever experienced. The highest temperature recorded was 37.1°C at Cheltenham on 3 August. The heatwave followed the passage of a cold front over the British Isles on 30 July. This gave some thunderstorms, with heavy rain in places. Some parts of southern England had their first rain for a fortnight. An anticyclone then established itself over eastern England, bringing sinking stable air and clear skies.

The effects of the 1990 heatwave were extreme. People were affected in many different ways.

A

Liverpool: all stock melts
The entire stock of a chocolate factory has melted during the recent hot spell...

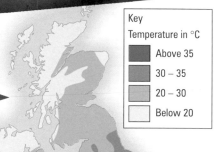

Windsor: residents urged to use their dishwater to water wilting trees

B *How a summer anticyclone is formed in the mid-latitudes.*

*The tropopause is the upper limit of the atmosphere

The variations in maximum temperature over Britain on 3 August 1990.

C

N

Key
Temperature in °C

■	Above 35
■	30 – 35
■	20 – 30
□	Below 20

SUN

Sun overhead Equator in March and September giving low pressure at Earth's surface

Sun overhead Tropic of Cancer in June

*Tropopause

Warm air returns to the Equator

Tropopause

As warm air moves north it cools and sinks

Rising low pressure air created by maximum heating from the sun overhead

Equator 0°

Tropic of Cancer 23½°N

Low pressure belt moves north from the Equator as relative position of the Sun moves north

Western Europe 55°N

High pressure anticyclone at surface

0   200km

1 Study **Source A**.
   a List the effects of the heatwave on people.
   b Brainstorm others and add them to your list.

2 Using **Source B**, explain how a summer anticyclone forms.

3 a Using **Source C**, describe the distribution of maximum temperatures on 3 August.
   b How does **Source E** help to explain the distribution?

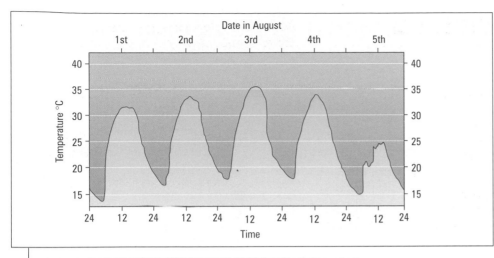

Graph for temperature at Maidenhead for the period 1–5 August 1990. It shows the diurnal (daily) changes for the period of the heatwave

D

By 0600 GMT on 4 August westerly winds were blowing over Scotland and Ireland. North-westerly winds were affecting England. High temperatures were, by now, being recorded only in the south-east of England. Even here it was much breezier than the previous day. The cold front continued to move south-eastwards and had almost reached the Kent coast by midnight.

On 5 August the highest recorded temperature was 25°C at Eastbourne. In Britain, the heatwave was over.

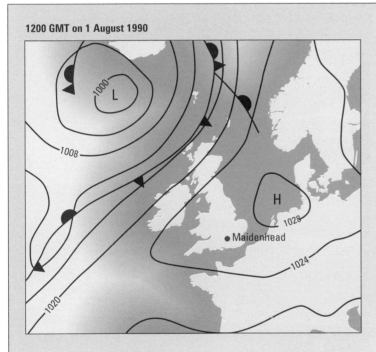

1200 GMT on 1 August 1990

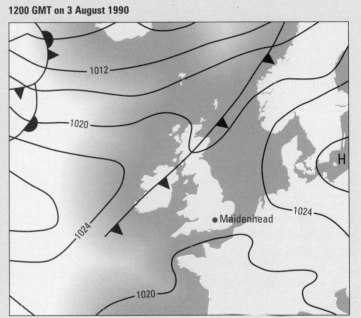

1200 GMT on 3 August 1990

Key

—1000—	Isobars: pressure in millibars	Cold front
H	Area of high pressure	Warm front
L	Area of low pressure	Occluded front

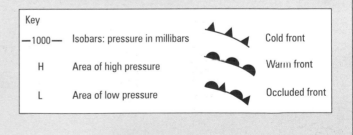

4 a Use **Source E** and other information from these pages to write a diary of the changes in the synoptic situation between 30 July and 5 August 1990.

b Compare your diary with the temperature changes shown in **Source D**.

5 a Compare this anticyclone with the one shown on pages 16 and 17 in terms of:
   • weather conditions
   • the effects on people.

b Explain the similarities and differences you have described.

The changing synoptic situation over north-west Europe during early August 1990. Note both the movements of the cold front and the centre of high pressure

E

1.8

Depths of a depression

How does a depression form?
What happens as a depression passes over?
How does a severe depression affect people and environments?
What importance do weather forecasts have for people?

Storm damage

Much of Britain's weather comes from the passage of **depressions**. These usually travel from west to east across the country, bringing changeable weather with rainfall as both **warm** and **cold fronts** pass over. Wind speeds are often high but depressions are rarely as destructive as the one experienced in October 1987. The storm caused destruction across Southern England from Cornwall through to Lincolnshire.

B *There is unlikely to be as deep a depression again for at least 200 years*

Thousands of roads and hundreds of railway lines blocked. Flights cancelled at Heathrow and Gatwick. Commuters badly affected.

Electricity cables down. Two weeks later 2000 homes still not reconnected.

Over 750 000 trees destroyed on National Trust property alone. Buildings from cottages to cathedrals suffered.

18 people died. The London Fire Brigade answered 6000 emergency calls.

15–16 October 1987

10.30 p.m. 300 yards from Seaford, Sussex, sea front. Wind about force 5. Spots of rain.

11.45 p.m. To bed on sixth and top floor of block of flats.

1 a.m. To sleep. Wind speed has increased marginally.

2.45 a.m. Awakened by rocking. It is me. I am rocking gently in bed. No, the bed is rocking me... The flat is being moved by what is now an audible wind...

3 a.m. There is a crack in the living room wall and it is moving... It is opening and closing about half an inch as the wind force surges.

3.45 a.m. We park ourselves with rugs on the stairs at about the second floor.

4 a.m. We are all three huddled in the lobby, standing facing the wall, heads covered with rugs... Somewhere upstairs glass breaks. Plaster and glass rattle down the narrow stairwell.

4.30 a.m. Loud crash from aloft. A larger shower of mixed debris clatters down the stairs.

7 a.m. Dawn. The wind is no longer fearsome. Still awesome... The flat's front door is still intact in its jamb. The glass panel is not. Through the gaps we can see devastation. Poor old grandfather (clock) lies face down in the hall... Double glazed sealed units have been savagely hurled about... Of the windward wall and the roof there remains little evidence.

8.30 a.m. The car has suffered. Flying debris has removed the offside windows. The bodywork has been attacked.

Source: John Crocker, *The Observer* 22 November 1987

A

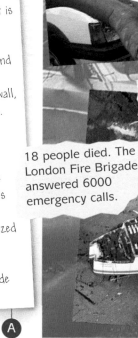

1 Study **Source A**.
a Describe the effects of the wind between 10.30 p.m. and 3 a.m.
b List the damage to:
(i) personal property
(ii) the structure of the building.
c Suggest why John and his companions reacted as they did.

2 Using **Source B** describe the damage caused by the high winds.

3 People complained that the severity of the storm had not been forecast.
a Suggest which kinds of damage could and could not have been avoided had there been a more accurate forecast.
b Explain your choices.

C

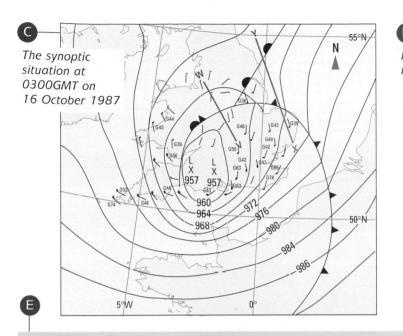

The synoptic situation at 0300GMT on 16 October 1987

D

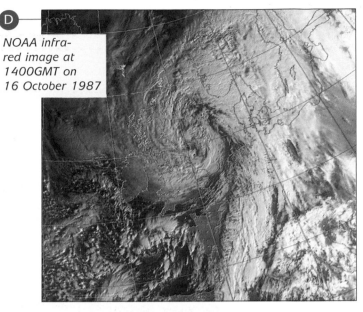

NOAA infra-red image at 1400GMT on 16 October 1987

E

a A cross-section through line X–Y on Source C

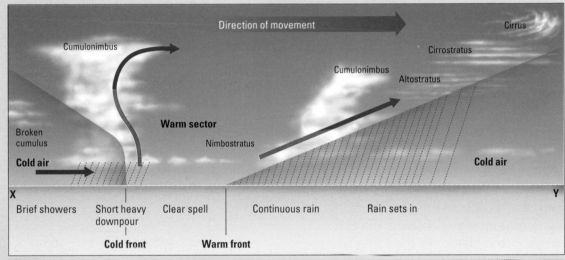

b A cross-section through line V–W on Source C. The cold front has moved more quickly than the warm front. The warm sector has been squeezed up at ground level to create an occluded front.

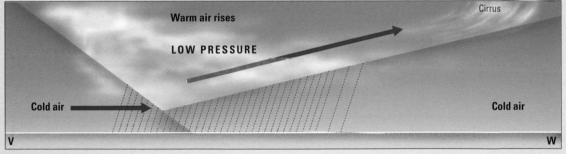

4 Using **Sources C** and **D** describe the depression in terms of:
a location
b the position of the warm and cold fronts.

5 Describe what happens as each front passes over in terms of:
a changes in air temperature
b changes in wind speed and direction.

6 a Using **Source D**, describe the distribution of cloud and rainfall.
b Explain this distribution using **Source E**.

7 Write a newspaper article about 'The great storm of 1987'. Locate the affected area. Include a description of the storm's effects, an explanation of its causes and an editorial in which you express your own feelings.

1.9 The eye of the storm

Where do hurricanes occur?
What is the life cycle of a hurricane?
How do hurricanes affect people?

Hurricane Andrew. A computer-generated image of the hurricane over the Gulf of Mexico

A

Awesome Andrew

B

The development of Andrew from a tropical depression to a hurricane

Before dawn on 24 August 1992 Hurricane Andrew hit the south-east coast of Florida. Within four hours it had become the most expensive natural disaster in the history of the USA. Twenty-six people were killed directly by its passage and another 39 died as a result of its indirect effects. A quarter of a million people were made temporarily homeless.

Hurricanes are intense low pressure systems. They form in the tropics when sea temperatures rise above 27°C. Warm, damp air spirals from the sea to the top of the hurricane. On the way up it releases heat, and condensation takes place. The air reaching the top is cool and dry. It is thrown great distances before dropping to sea level. Here it warms and picks up moisture. The whole cycle begins again. This will continue for as long as there is a warm sea area to keep the process going.

1 a Using **Source A** and an atlas, describe the location of Hurricane Andrew.
b Describe the appearance of the hurricane in **Source A**.
c Using the information in **Source B**, identify when **Source A** was taken.

2 Study **Source B**.
a Describe the route taken by Andrew from 17 to 28 August 1992.
b When did Andrew become a hurricane?
c Look at the table on page 23. Describe the characteristics Andrew would have when it was first named as a hurricane. How did these change as it progressed to Category 4?
d Explain why Hurricane Andrew quickly died down on 27 August.

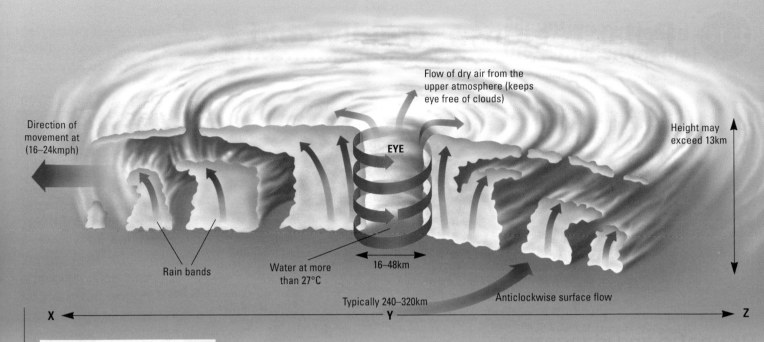

 A section through a hurricane similar to Andrew

Labels on the diagram:
- Flow of dry air from the upper atmosphere (keeps eye free of clouds)
- Direction of movement at (16–24kmph)
- EYE
- Height may exceed 13km
- Rain bands
- Water at more than 27°C
- 16–48km
- Typically 240–320km
- Anticlockwise surface flow
- X — Y — Z

Storm type	Central pressure (millibars)	Winds (knots)	Storm surge (metres)	Typical damage	Example/ location /damage
Tropical depression		34			
Tropical storm		35–64	<1.2		
Hurricane category 1	>980	65–82	1.2–1.6	Minimal	Allison (1995), Florida , minimal
Category 2	965–979	83–86	1.7–2.5	Moderate	Bob (1991), New England, US $1.5 billion
Category 3	945–964	97–113	2.6–3.8	Extensive	Alicia (1983), Texas, US $2.4 billion
Category 4	920–944	114–134	3.9–5.5	Extreme	Andrew (1992), Florida, US $25 billion
Category 5	<920	>134	>5.5	Catastrophic	Camille (1969), Gulf Coast, US $5.2 billion

Source: Geographical Magazine October 1995

E Some tropical storms and their effects

D Wind speed and air pressure across section X–Y in Source C

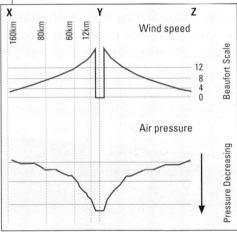

Labels: X, Y, Z; 160km, 80km, 60km, 12km; Wind speed; Beaufort Scale 12 8 4 0; Air pressure; Pressure Decreasing

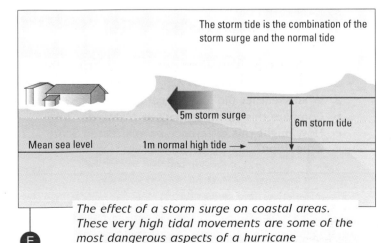

Labels: The storm tide is the combination of the storm surge and the normal tide; 5m storm surge; 6m storm tide; Mean sea level; 1m normal high tide

F The effect of a storm surge on coastal areas. These very high tidal movements are some of the most dangerous aspects of a hurricane

3 On a copy of **Source C** use information from **Source D** to label:
a places of relatively high and low wind speeds
b a place of calm
c the position of most rapid pressure drop.

4 Annotate your copy of **Source C** to explain why a hurricane is described as being self-generating.

5 Write a paragraph to explain fully the life cycle of a hurricane.

6 a Suggest the effects of a hurricane on people and their possessions.
b Produce a TV or radio broadcast advising people what to do as a hurricane approaches.

1.11 City heat

Hot on the inside

Have you ever been in a city on a hot summer's day and wished for the cool countryside? Have you noticed how quickly snow melts or rain evaporates from city pavements? Have you felt the heat of traffic fumes or had difficulty breathing due to pollution?

These are all features of modern cities which create local climates, or **heat islands**, of their own. The idea of an urban 'heat island' is not, however, new.

In 1820, Luke Howard announced that he had discovered London's 'heat island'. He blamed the difference in temperature on the use of coal. Today, coal burning hardly exists in towns and cities but heat islands remain.

A **Fact file ...** **London's coal problem**

John Evelyn (1620–1706) wrote a paper against the use of coal in manufacturing. He wrote: 'For in all other places the air is most serene and pure, it is here eclipsed with such cloud of Sulphur as the Sun itself ... is hardly able to penetrate it, and the weary traveller sooner smells than sees the City'.

1 Dark brick buildings, concrete and tarmac store heat which is released at night.

2 Drainage systems remove rain quickly so less heat is used to evaporate water. The heat can warm the buildings.

3 Housing estates reduce wind speed at the surface. Warm air can build up.

10 Concentrations of people in cities add heat to the air.

9 Rivers can provide cool areas as heat is absorbed or used in evaporation.

8 High rise buildings and narrow streets reduce wind speed and allow warm air to build up.

7 Large parks with grass, trees and poor drainage use up heat in evaporation giving cool spots in the city.

6 Traffic pollution can add heat to urban air as well as CO_2, SO_2 and smoke.

Central Business District (CBD) – offices, shops, high rise buildings.

Inner-city – terraced houses, high rise flats, narrow streets, old factories, redevelopment, inner ring roads, small parks.

Suburbia – semi-detached and detached private housing, large gardens, large parks, outer ring roads, small shopping centres.

Council housing – edge-of-city, industrial estates, out-of-town shopping centres, business parks.

4 Central heating from shops and offices in the CBD can warm the air in the streets.

Countryside – villages

The urban–rural fringe

B

Urban land use affects the climate

5 Warm air from the CBD can rise causing convection rain and isolated thunderstorms.

1 What image of London does **Source A** create?

2 On a copy of **Source B** match the labels with the locations A–J.

3 Imagine you have been asked to advise on the building of a new town. The planners wish to avoid heat islands. What advice would you give?

D *A typical October evening: Glasgow's heat island*

Key

- ▨ CBD shops and offices
- ▓ Industrial areas
- ▨ Densely built-up area
- ☐ Less densely built-up area
- ▨ Open space
- 4 Isotherm—line joining places of the same temperature

E *Glasgow city centre*

Prevailing wind

River Clyde

0   3km

Glasgow by night

As you have seen, there are many reasons why a city can have higher temperatures than the countryside. The seasons can also have an influence. On cold autumn and winter nights heat released from building materials and additional central heating can produce a large difference compared to a rapidly cooling countryside. This can also occur on calm, sunny summer days when, with no cool breeze, heat build-up within the city can be oppressive.

Wind direction can also move the heat island away from the main source. With a prevailing wind direction from the south-west, cities in the UK often have warmer air moved from the Central Business District (CBD) towards the north-east.

4 Study **Source D**. On a copy of the section A–B:
a mark the land use changes
b add symbols or drawings to show each land use.
c Using **Source C** to help you, mark:
   (i) areas likely to produce high temperatures
   (ii) areas likely to produce cooler temperatures.
d Explain your choice of areas.

5 a Above your section A–B draw a temperature graph using the same horizontal scale.
b Describe and suggest reasons for the changes in temperature:
   (i) along the section A–B
   (ii) across Glasgow in general.

6 Which features shown in **Source E** may contribute to Glasgow's heat island? Explain your answers.

1 Give us a break

Give us a break

How does the weather affect your life around the school? Could the school environment be planned to take better account of the weather? Are facilities sited in the best possible locations in the school yard? Could you advise your school on more suitable siting of facilities or even suggest new ones?

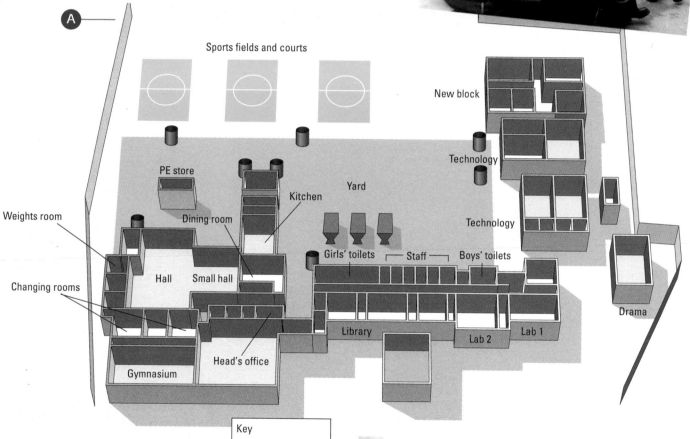

What might be the effect of your school buildings on:
- air temperatures
- shade at different times of the day
- wind patterns. . .
. . . and how might these affect your life at school?

1 Negotiate a suitable area of study with your teacher. It could, for example, be an investigation into the siting of such varied facilities as litter bins and picnic tables.

2 Decide which aspects of the weather and the school's local climate affect your chosen facility.

3 Plan how you will collect your evidence and the instruments you will need to carry out your study.

4 Collect the evidence.

5 Refine and present your evidence.

6 Use your evidence in order to make recommendations to your School Council.

Natural environments

KEY IDEAS

Natural environments can be perceived as environmental systems which operate at a variety of scales.

Ecosystems can be perceived as a resource for human benefit.

Changes occur in ecosystems as a result of natural processes and/or people's activities. The consequences of such change may go beyond the immediate ecosystem.

The impact of people's activities on ecosystems needs careful management.

2.1 All systems go

A *Ecosystems exist at a variety of scales and are influenced by many factors, including landscape and climate*

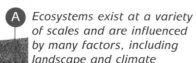

1 Tundra, N. Russia

3 Savanna, Ethiopia

4 Rainforest, Borneo

2 Po Delta, Italy

Carnivores like stoats, weasels and tawny owls are within the tree and on the ground.

Birds like finches and sparrows feed on the seeds produced by the plants.

B

A complex ecosystem exists within this group of trees

Humus is the decayed organic material which forms the top of layer of the soil. It is a rich store of nutrients or food for the trees.

Materials like water, carbon dioxide, sunlight and weathered rock material come into the system.

Soluble nutrients like calcium and iron are washed out of the system and some gases like methane leave as a result of the functions of the plant and animal life.

Animals and plants which die are decomposed by microbes, bacteria, fungi and other life forms.

Within the tree, the Sun's energy is transferred into food energy by photosynthesis.

People and environments

We rely on our environment to meet our needs. People can be regarded as **stewards** of the environment, looking after it for future generations. The way we use the environment needs to be **sustainable**. We depend on it so we must take care not to destroy it.

1 Study **Source A**. For each ecosystem photograph:
a use an atlas to describe its location
b describe the scene
c suggest how the ecosystem could be used by people
d explain to what extent this use of the ecosystem would be sustainable.

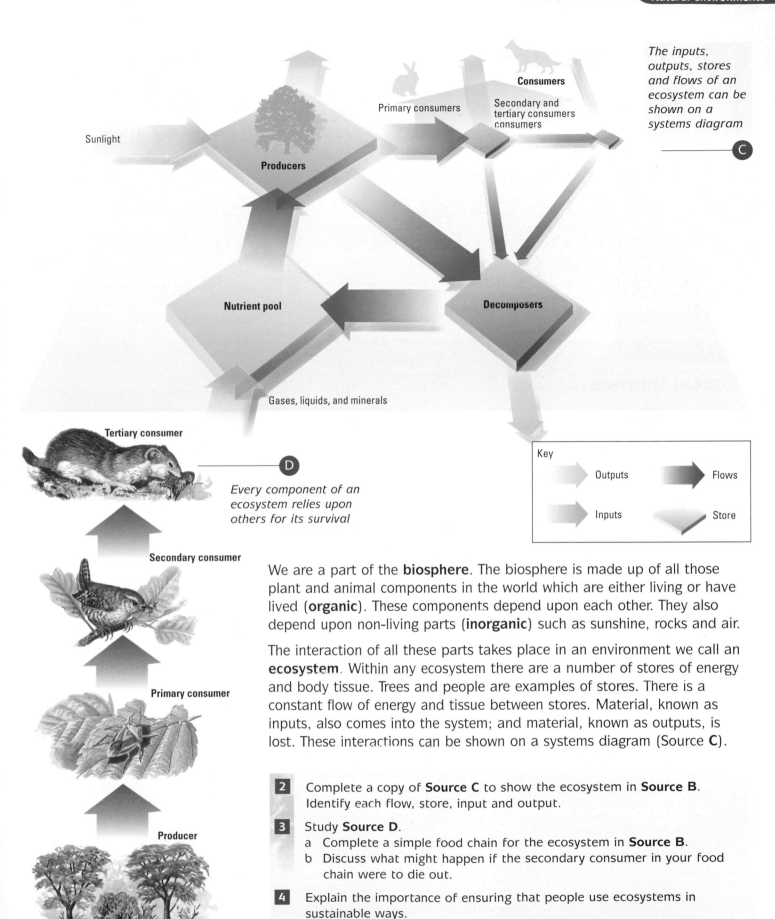

The inputs, outputs, stores and flows of an ecosystem can be shown on a systems diagram

Consumers

Primary consumers

Secondary and tertiary consumers consumers

Sunlight

Producers

Nutrient pool

Decomposers

Gases, liquids, and minerals

Tertiary consumer

D

Every component of an ecosystem relies upon others for its survival

Key

Outputs   Flows

Inputs   Store

Secondary consumer

Primary consumer

Producer

We are a part of the **biosphere**. The biosphere is made up of all those plant and animal components in the world which are either living or have lived (**organic**). These components depend upon each other. They also depend upon non-living parts (**inorganic**) such as sunshine, rocks and air.

The interaction of all these parts takes place in an environment we call an **ecosystem**. Within any ecosystem there are a number of stores of energy and body tissue. Trees and people are examples of stores. There is a constant flow of energy and tissue between stores. Material, known as inputs, also comes into the system; and material, known as outputs, is lost. These interactions can be shown on a systems diagram (Source **C**).

2 Complete a copy of **Source C** to show the ecosystem in **Source B**. Identify each flow, store, input and output.

3 Study **Source D**.
a Complete a simple food chain for the ecosystem in **Source B**.
b Discuss what might happen if the secondary consumer in your food chain were to die out.

4 Explain the importance of ensuring that people use ecosystems in sustainable ways.

31

2.2 The changing tropics

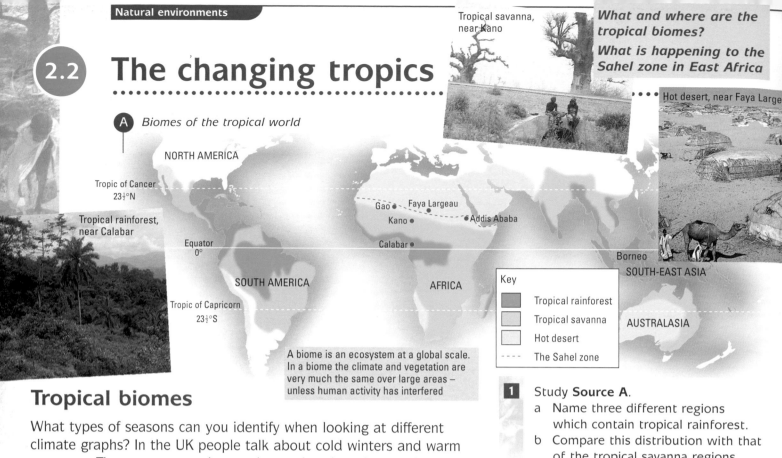

A Biomes of the tropical world

Tropical savanna, near Kano

Hot desert, near Faya Large

NORTH AMERICA

Tropic of Cancer 23½°N

Gao • • Faya Largeau
Kano • • Addis Ababa

Tropical rainforest, near Calabar

Equator 0°

Calabar •

Borneo

SOUTH-EAST ASIA

SOUTH AMERICA

AFRICA

Tropic of Capricorn 23½°S

AUSTRALASIA

Key

▨	Tropical rainforest
▥	Tropical savanna
☐	Hot desert
----	The Sahel zone

A biome is an ecosystem at a global scale. In a biome the climate and vegetation are very much the same over large areas – unless human activity has interfered

Tropical biomes

What types of seasons can you identify when looking at different climate graphs? In the UK people talk about cold winters and warm summers. The seasons are clear and are related to changes in temperature.

Tropical **biomes** are very different from those in temperate latitudes like the UK. Temperatures are much higher between the Tropics of Cancer and Capricorn. They nearly always average more than 20°C. Variation in temperature is less significant to the people, plants and animals living there. What matters more is whether the season is wet or dry.

1 Study **Source A**.
  a Name three different regions which contain tropical rainforest.
  b Compare this distribution with that of the tropical savanna regions.

2 Use **Source B** and the photographs in **Source A** to:
  a complete a table comparing temperature and rainfall at the four climate stations.
  b Suggest how the natural vegetation adapts to the changes in climate across North Africa.

0° Equator	5°N	10°N	15°N	20°N

Decreasing rainfall →

THE SAHEL ZONE

Precipitation (mm) / Average monthly temperature (°C)

Calabar, Nigeria	Kano, Nigeria	Gao, Mali	Faya Largeau, Chad
Total = 3070mm	Total = 841mm	Total = 271mm	Total = 23mm
Trees dominate	Fewer trees/more grassland	Open grassland/scrub	Desert

Savanna woodland

Savanna grassland

South   North

BIOME			
Tropical rainforest	→	Tropical savanna	→ Hot desert

B

Travelling north across Africa: from forest to desert

Survival in the savanna ecosystem

C

1 Elephant breaking down trees and bush
2 Buffalo browsing among the tall grass
3 Wildebeest grazing the shorter grass left by the buf
4 Zebra eating the grass left by the wildebeest
5 Gazelles cropping the short turf
6 Wart hogs tearing up the turf
7 Cheetah surveying hunting grounds

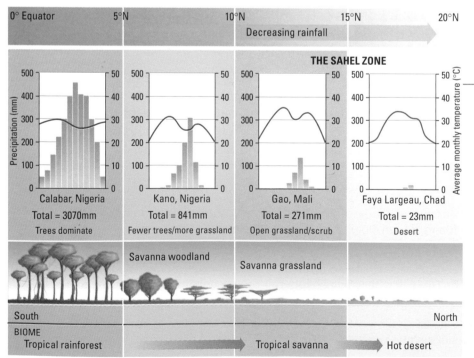

The Sahel – Africa continues to dry up

The Sahel zone of Africa stretches from Mauritania in the west to Ethiopia in the east. It is not a fixed area. It is a belt of land which, in recent years, has not received enough rainfall to maintain the savanna grassland. With less rainfall the grassland has become dry scrub. Where total rainfall is less than 250mm, only plants and animals adapted to **desert** conditions can survive.

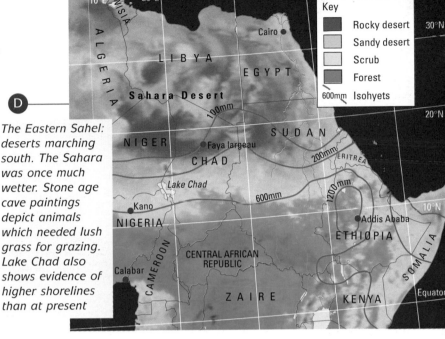

D

The Eastern Sahel: deserts marching south. The Sahara was once much wetter. Stone age cave paintings depict animals which needed lush grass for grazing. Lake Chad also shows evidence of higher shorelines than at present

3
a Use **Source C** to produce a food web. It should include two primary producers, two primary consumers (herbivores) and a secondary consumer (carnivore).
b Suggest how the savanna ecosystem might change as less rainfall is received.

4 Study the information in **Source D**.
a Describe the vegetation pattern.
b Explain how this relates to the rainfall pattern.
c What evidence is there that North Africa was once much wetter?

5 Study **Source E**.
a For how many years was rainfall above and below average between 1930 and 1949?
b Compare this pattern with the periods between:
(i) 1950 and 1968
(ii) 1969 and 1990.
c How have recent changes in rainfall affected people?

E *Rainfall changes in the Sahel 1930–90*

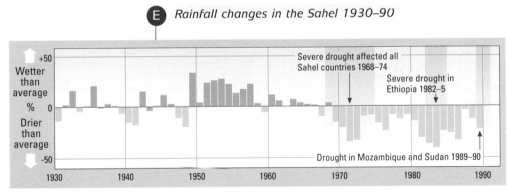

6 Study **Source F**.
a What are the causes of 'desertification'? How is this different from 'land degradation'?
b Explain how a run of dry years can affect people in the Sahel.
c What choices do people have in this situation?

7 'Desertification and land degradation in the Sahel affect both **LEDCs** and **MEDCs**.' Discuss this hypothesis.

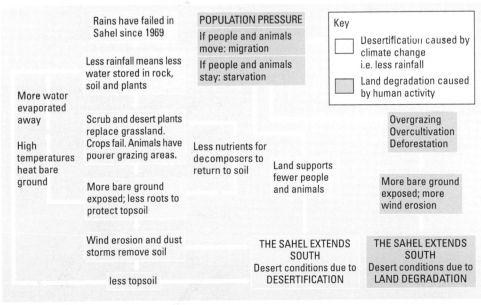

F

The changing Sahel

2.3 Surviving in Ethiopia

Every day, Jeggo has to climb a mountain just to survive.

Every day Jeggo goes up and down a mountain to get water for her family. For a 7 year old, it's a real struggle. When full, the water container she carries on her back is almost as heavy as another child of her age.

Jeggo lives in a mountainous region in Ethiopia where water is scarce. When the rains fail, people are unable to grow their crops. Many starve.

Could you go without food for 24 hours to help someone like Jeggo? If so, why not join the thousands of others throughout the country who'll be taking part in the World Vision 24 Hour Famine on March 8th.

Among other lifesaving projects worldwide, the money raised will help save the lives of people like Jeggo in Ethiopia by providing them with food, proper irrigation, fresh water supplies and basic healthcare.

Send for your FREE 24 Hour Famine Kit today – containing everything you need to make your Famine Day a success, including a sponsor form and a special Countdown Calendar.

24 HOUR FAMINE

24 hours in your life is all it takes to give someone like Jeggo a future.

A

Why is Ethiopia so poor?

Desertification is not the real problem in Ethiopia. Very few people live in or near the Sahel. It is in the rainy, hilly areas, where people can survive, that the real threats lie.

For over 3000 years Ethiopia was a wealthy area with a unique, rich culture. Today news about Ethiopia is often tragic. In the last 30 years we have heard about the great distress caused by drought, famine and civil war. Of the 27 million people living in Africa who need emergency aid, over half are in Ethiopia. Jeggo is one of these.

Ethiopia is a land of contrasts. In some parts the rain is four times the amount received in the UK. In others it seldom and is drought-prone. Rivers can be dr flood, with heavy rainfall during the we season removing topsoil. It is the most mountainous country in Africa with hot tropical valleys and cool rainy highland

B

Problem 1: Drought
In the 1973 drought over 200 000 people died. The famine of 1984–5 was the result of drought and war. At least half a million people died.

Problem 2: Population pressure
The population of 54 million is doubling every 25 years. Unless the birth rate is reduced the country will always lack enough food. Only 71 per cent of the population have an adequate diet.

Survival – a problem for the people

C

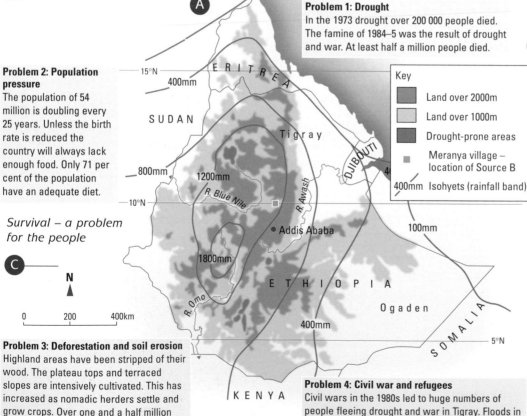

Key

	Land over 2000m
	Land over 1000m
	Drought-prone areas
■	Meranya village – location of Source B
400mm	Isohyets (rainfall band)

Problem 3: Deforestation and soil erosion
Highland areas have been stripped of their wood. The plateau tops and terraced slopes are intensively cultivated. This has increased as nomadic herders settle and grow crops. Over one and a half million tonnes of soil is washed into the Blue Nile every year during the wet season.

Problem 4: Civil war and refugees
Civil wars in the 1980s led to huge numbers of people fleeing drought and war in Tigray. Floods in Sudan caused many to enter Ethiopia after 1988. The population is difficult to organize into settled communities. Eritrea gained independence in 1993 making Ethiopia a land-locked country.

1 Study **Source A**. Describe and explain Jeggo's daily routine.

2
a Describe the landscape in **Source B**.
b To what extent is this the result of human activity?

3 Study **Source C**.
a Describe the variety of physical environments in Ethiopia.
b Basic human needs include water, food and shelter. Suggest why they are difficult to meet in Ethiopia.

4 Suggest what needs to change if Ethiopia is to produce surplus food so that it can develop its economy.

5V-MAG

LOFOODPR

PRA is central to FARM's work in Africa. PRA is about working with the local people. A trained person helps them analyse their own conditions and they choose their own ways of improving them. It is low cost aid which causes little disruption to everyday life but allows lasting progress as the people begin to help themselves.

Working with the people: Participatory Rural Appraisal (PRA)

E

D Food aid is dropped to hungry Ethiopians but this help can only last a few days

PRA in action. The women of Lemen Warko make a map of their village showing the different crops that are grown. The men are more interested in laying out boundaries

FARM-Africa: helping people to help themselves

In the media we often see wealthy countries sending food to LEDCs. This approach, however, cannot help a country to develop in the long term unless sustainable solutions are found. Then they will not need to rely on emergency food supplies being sent in.

FARM-Africa is a non-governmental organization (NGO). The initials stand for *Food and Agricultural Research Management*. FARM is using its resources to improve life for people in Ethiopia. Many women are involved in FARM's Dairy Goat Projects. One of these is Naime Alito (Source **F**).

5 a Study **Source E** and compare the FARM approach using PRA to that illustrated in **Source D**.
   b Which approach to aid is more helpful to Ethiopia in the long term? Explain your answer.

6 Read about Naime in **Source F**.
   a What does Naime say about the traditional role of women in Ethiopia?
   b How might the nature of Naime's family affect her efforts to survive?
   c Suggest how the goat project has helped Naime improve her quality of life and her status in society.

7 FARM-Africa is advertising for an 18-year-old student to spend a year helping people in Ethiopia. The job is voluntary but all expenses are paid.
   a Suggest ways in which FARM could advertise the job opportunity.
   b Select one way and produce an advertisement.

F *Naime Alito explains how the Dairy Goat Project empowers women in Ethiopia*

This project has changed what women usually do. Earlier women's projects encouraged us to make stoves, grow vegetables or sew – things we were already doing as part of our domestic chores. This project gave me the chance to go beyond that and earn money for the future. The project gave me two goats on credit, which produced ten offspring in four years and helped to pay for medical treatment for my husband before he died.

I can grow just enough food for my family to get through the dry season but we have poor rains here. Owning livestock brings me status in the community. Last year I sold goats to buy a bullock and saved money for more equipment. Now I can plough the land instead of using hand tools. My small land-holding has grown to nearly an acre as I can produce more food. Before I could only cultivate half an acre (0.2 **hectares**).

I have been trained to be a paravet; I am on call to visit the group's sick goats. People value my service and call me when the goats are sick. We have regular meetings to discuss the goats and community interests. Women are beginning to help with important decisions. Even men come to me asking for advice which would never have happened without the project.

Source: Adapted from *FARM-Africa,* Summer 1996

Naime Alito and her family

2.4 The unspoiled rainforest

What is the rainforest ecosystem?
How is the rainforest ecosystem traditionally used as a resource?
How else may the rainforest be perceived as a resource?

The rainforest system

It is difficult to imagine from Columbus' account that the rainforests are fragile. They rely on the rapid recycling of **nutrients** at ground level for their survival. Here the atmosphere is steamy. As soon as plant material falls to the ground it is attacked by fungi and bacteria. This creates **humus** which provides nutrients to be taken up by the shallow tree roots. Some additional nutrient material comes from the **weathering** of the rock on which the soil rests. The soil is a weak store of nutrients.

Intense sunshine absorbed by the upper layers of the forest provides the energy for rapid plant growth and high rainfall totals supply ample water. Although rainfall is heavy the soil is protected by its vegetation cover and nutrient loss by **leaching** is only about 1 per cent. If the vegetation were removed, however, the nutrients would quickly be removed from the soil. The forest would not be able to grow back.

I never beheld so fair a thing: trees beautiful and green and different from ours, with flowers and fruits each according to their kind, many birds and little birds which sing so sweetly.

Christopher Columbus

A

The unspoiled rainforest gives rise to a variety of feelings

Emergent layer
Where very tall trees are scattered, having broken through the canopy

Canopy layer
A continuous layer of tree crowns where much rain is caught

B

Definite layers are formed in areas of mature rainforest

Young trees
Small trees which make rapid vertical growth towards the light

Shrub layer
Low bushes and shrubs grow where there is little sunlight

Ground layer
Decomposers, fungi and humus

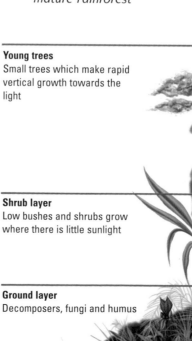

1 Using the world map on page 32 describe the location of the world's rainforests.

2 Look at the photograph on page 29 and **Source A** on this page.
a Choose five words which best describe your feelings towards the rainforest scene.
b How much do you agree with the views of Christopher Columbus?

3 Study **Source B**.
a Describe the vertical structure of the rainforest.
b Suggest how the need for sunlight influences the forest structure.

4 a For the rainforest identify three inputs, two stores, three flows and one output.
b Produce a systems diagram for the rainforest.

Not long ago we were happy.
Things were good.
Our fish was clean.
Our food was pure.

We live by getting palm heart, by getting **sago**.
We eat different types of animals.
We are content making sago.

There are many medicines,
many hunting poisons here in the forest.

If the land is preserved like this...
all the animals happy to eat the fruit of the trees.
Satisfied life.
They eat the fruits.
We eat them.

We go out with blowpipe, get something,
return... ah!
Content to eat, content with life.

This is a good life
Source: Thoughts by Dawat Lupung

C

It is possible for people to meet all their needs from the forest without destroying it

Key

■ Rainforest
▨ Deforested areas
☁ Cloud
Grey smoke from burning

N
▲

The original inhabitants of Borneo are given the group name of Dayak. In 1990, the population of the island was 3.6 million of which the Dayaks represented one-third. They live mainly in rural, forested areas. The Penan are a nomadic group of Dayaks.

D *Satellite image of an area of rainforest in Sarawak*

5 Using the map on page 32 describe the location of Borneo.

6 The Penan are a nomadic group.
   a What is a nomad?
   b Use **Source C** to explain the importance of the forest to the Penan people.

7 Look at **Source D**.
   a What proportion of forest has been removed: 1, 10, 25, or 50 per cent?
   b Describe the pattern of areas which have been logged.
   c Suggest which areas may be the next to be logged. Explain your answer.

F *Timber exports as a percentage of all Borneo's exports, 1991*

Political area	Timber as a % of total exports
South Kalimantan	90
Central Kalimantan	75
West Kalimantan	68
Sabah	32
Sarawak	27
East Kalimantan	11
Brunei	1

8 Study **Source E**.
   a On a political map of Borneo draw a choropleth map to show the information.
   b Describe the pattern shown by your map.
   c Discuss why different areas may rely more heavily on timber exports than others.

2.5 Rainforest destruction

Going ... going ... gone

The cleared forest soil is exposed to the full force of the rain. It has already been broken up by the use of heavy machinery and the dragging of logs to the rivers. The river banks are also destroyed by the dragging of logs. The rain washes soil particles away. These pollute the rivers. Those nutrients that remain in the soil are rapidly removed by leaching. The chances of forest **regeneration** are small.

A

For every tree taken from the forest another nineteen are destroyed

B *Japanese lumber imports, 1960–90*

Year	Lumber* imports (in 1000m^3)
1960	6 390
1965	16 920
1970	42 364
1975	38 262
1980	43 083
1985	34 076
1990	28 999

* All wood products

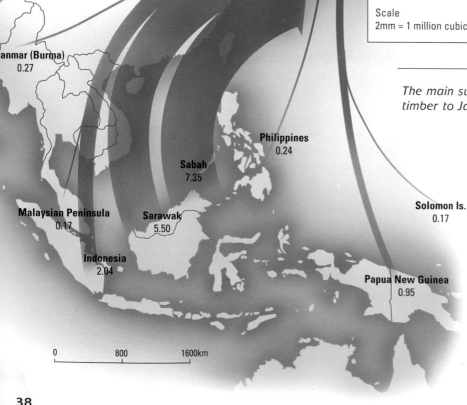

Tropical Latin America 0.17

Tropical Africa 0.25

Myanmar (Burma) 0.27

JAPAN

N

Key

Wood exports in million cubic metres

Scale
2mm = 1 million cubic metres

C

The main suppliers of tropical timber to Japan

Philippines 0.24

Sabah 7.35

Malaysian Peninsula 0.17

Sarawak 5.50

Solomon Is. 0.17

Indonesia 2.04

Papua New Guinea 0.95

0   800   1600km

1 Study **Source A**.
   a Describe the activities shown.
   b Explain how these affect the rainforest and its soil.
   c Suggest why regeneration of the forest is unlikely.

2 Draw a graph to display the information in **Source B**.

3 a Using **Source C**, place the suppliers of tropical timber to Japan in rank order.
   b What are the implications of your findings for the island of Borneo?

A peaceful protest against logging

D

Thoughts of Dawat Lupung

This land is our origins...

How can the government say it isn't our land?

We don't like the company to destroy the forest any more; they make the water muddy, we become ill, we get TB, we get eye illness, we get malaria, we get killed on the bulldozer roads...

There is not enough to eat. many people will die – no food. Soon many people die.

These plants are our medicines, if we ask for medicines from the government, they give us Panadol*.

I wanted to talk to the police about land to be saved for us to stay alive.

People who talk go to jail.

The water muddy, the fish are dead Can't drink the water any more, muddy, terrible, no good.

Trees that are cut down were once the shelter of hornbills, the home of gibbons, the home of langur, the home of every single kind of animal that lives up high.

* Commercial painkiller

*Using **biosphere reserves** is one possible means of rainforest protection*

E

| Unprotected forest | Settlement permitted | Farming and wood gathering permitted | Hunting and collecting permitted | Protected rainforest |

Dawat Lupung was born in 1963. He first contacted people other than his own in his teens. Since then he has watched the logging companies destroy everything he holds sacred. His foods, medicines, building materials, the temples of his gods and the burial sites of his ancestors have all been affected. In 1976 the government made Dawat and his family squatters and forced them to move to a **resettlement site**. They were expected to make **rattan** mats and baskets to sell to tourists. The 'better life' the government promised became hunger, malnutrition, infectious diseases and a longing for home and a nomadic way of life.

In 1987 Dawat joined the Penan struggle to protect the forest by helping to erect peaceful blockades across logging roads. He was handcuffed, beaten by the police and imprisoned for 30 days.

In February 1990 he tried unsuccessfully to prevent his father's grave from being bulldozed...

4 Study **Source D**.
a Explain how Dawat Lupung's life has been affected by the logging companies. Consider his home, diet, health and freedom.
b Comment on the actions of Dawat Lupung. What would you have done in his position?

5 Study **Source E**.
a Explain how a biosphere reserve operates.
b Suggest how the use of a biosphere reserve would affect:
(i) rates of rainforest destruction
(ii) the lives of people like Dawat Lupung.

6 Discuss other means by which the rainforest might be managed. Which would you favour? Explain your choice.

2.6 Northern extremes

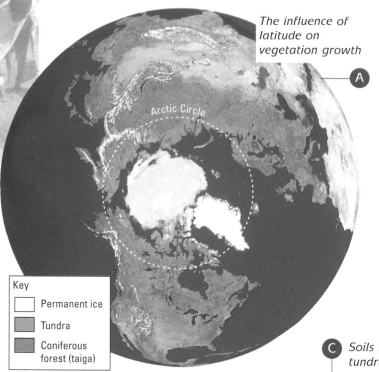

The influence of latitude on vegetation growth

A

Arctic Circle

Key
- Permanent ice
- Tundra
- Coniferous forest (taiga)

The tundra...

The arctic climate is harsh. **Lichens** and **mosses** manage to grow in temperatures as low as as -20°C. Most other forms of life must adapt to survive in this cold desert. They do so in different ways. Many plants, for example, flower and seed quickly. Most animals migrate. The reindeer spend summer in the **tundra**, calving and grazing. Then, at the end of this brief season, they gather together in herds and move south for as much as 1000km to the forests of the **taiga** where they live for the winter.

Climate figures for Archangel, Russia												
	J	F	M	A	M	J	J	A	S	O	N	D
Temperature (°C)	-14	-16	-11	-1	8	12	15	12	8	2	-4	-13
Precipitation (mm)	34	24	27	31	47	52	59	54	57	57	49	48
Total precipitation = 539mm												

C Soils sustain the tundra life forms

B Light and heat are precious in these latitudes

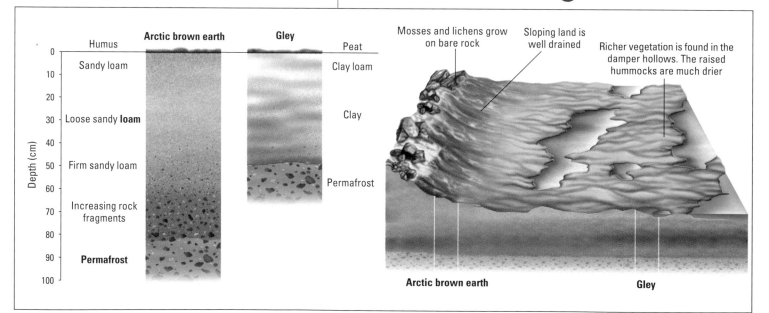

Mosses and lichens grow on bare rock

Sloping land is well drained

Richer vegetation is found in the damper hollows. The raised hummocks are much drier

Arctic brown earth

Gley

Arctic brown earth
- Humus
- Sandy loam
- Loose sandy **loam**
- Firm sandy loam
- Increasing rock fragments
- **Permafrost**

Gley
- Peat
- Clay loam
- Clay
- Permafrost

Depth (cm)

---

1 Study **Source A**. Describe the distribution of the tundra vegetation.

2
a Use **Source B** to produce a climate graph for Archangel.
b Describe the patterns shown on your graph.
c To what extent would you agree that this is a 'cold desert'? Explain your answer.

3 Study **Source C**.
a Describe the differences in location between the two soils.
b Use the following headings to describe the gley soil: depth, soil structure and plant cover.
c How does the arctic brown soil differ from the gley?
d Suggest how location may explain these differences.

... and its ecosystems

According to reports from Russia's north-eastern Chukotskiy territory, as many as 30 000 reindeer are at risk because heavy rains a month ago were followed by freezing temperatures and blizzards that have covered their traditional winter grazing areas in a thick sheet of ice ... Igor Cheston, director of the World Wide Fund for Nature in Russia, said that the crisis was affecting tame reindeer herds as well as those living in the wild which both feed on Arctic moss that usually sustains them until the spring thaw ... A desperate bulletin released by Russia's Industry of Emergency Situations yesterday reported that more than 1000 reindeer had died in the past 24 hours. Since the famine was first reported over the weekend more than 4500 animals had perished.

Source: The Times, 12 December 1996

4 Study **Source E**:
  a Draw a simple food chain involving reindeer.
  b Explain any changes which might take place if there was:
    (i) a large increase in the wolf population
    (ii) a large increase in the lemming and arctic hare populations.
  c Which animal is unlikely to be affected by a change in the carnivore population? Explain your choice.

5 Study **Source F**.
  a Describe the weather conditions.
  b How did these affect the reindeer?
  c What might be the effect of such changes on the lives of people?

6 Use evidence from these pages to comment on the suitability of the tundra for human life.

D *Conditions suitable for rich plant growth exist for only a short season*

E *A rich variety of life exists in this environment*

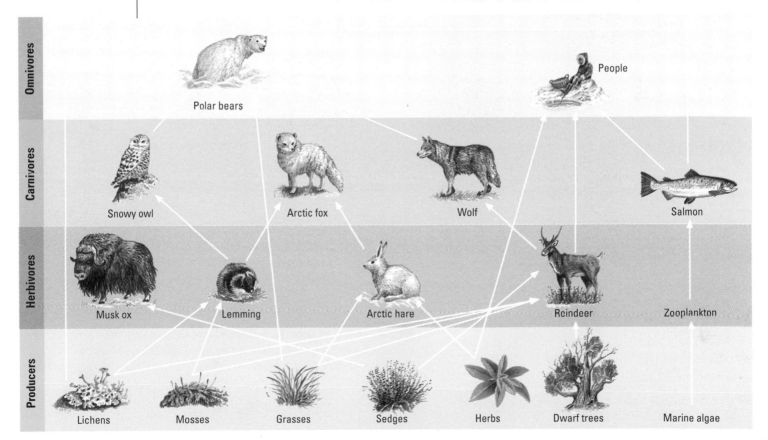

2.7 Life in the Russian tundra

How do decisions made beyond the tundra affect the ecosystem and its people?

How might the effects on the tundra ecosystem be managed?

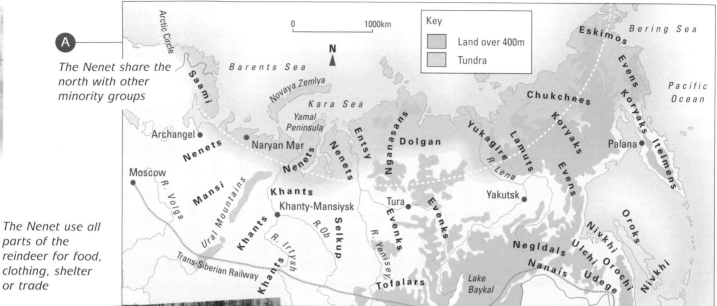

A The Nenet share the north with other minority groups

Key
Land over 400m
Tundra

B The Nenet use all parts of the reindeer for food, clothing, shelter or trade

History of the People: Part One – Before Communism

Parts of the area were protected from Europeans by the Ural Mountains. The Nenet were completely self-sufficient and had no need to move beyond their traditional migration routes.

The first explorers came in the mid-seventeenth century. They were interested in the mineral and fur wealth. Many nomads were treated brutally by these outsiders.

A large buck is ritually slaughtered and then disembowelled. Members of the Nenet tribe crowd around to feast on the raw flesh, the adults washing each mouthful down with vodka. Once everyone has eaten their fill, the animal is skinned and the remaining meat is preserved and stored. Nothing is wasted.

Source: Andrew North, *Geographical Magazine*, April 1994.

A northern Russian village community at the beginning of the twentieth century

A sustainable lifestyle

The Nenet are nomadic herders of reindeer, which are relatives of the caribou. They live in the tundra of the Russian Federation and, with a population of 34 000, are the largest of the 26 tribes that make up the officially recognized **'Northern Minorities'**.

1
a Using **Source A**, describe the location of the Nenet lands.
b Suggest and explain a seasonal pattern of Nenet movement.

2 Using the information on this page, explain how the Nenet life-style may be regarded as a sustainable use of the tundra.

A raised oil pipeline in Siberia

Huge areas of both tundra and taiga have been destroyed by Soviet industrial development.

Careless mineral extraction from 1979 to 1989 has destroyed 20 million hectares of reindeer pasture.

Fall-out from the Novaya Zemlya atomic weapons test site has severely affected traditional life.

The Communist regime has destroyed 30 per cent of the taiga forest.

History of the People: Part Two – The Communist Era

Changes in the Russian north after the 1917 revolution were the result of the political beliefs of people in Moscow. All surplus wealth was confiscated and each herder was allowed just four reindeer. Many herders perished as a result of starvation.

From the late 1920s they were forced to seek work in **state farms** and to live in permanent settlements. Here they received wages three or four times less than incoming people.

By the 1950s the government had banned the use of native languages and children were forced to attend state schools. Alcoholism and high suicide rates affected most tribes of the northern minorities.

Life expectancy of members of the Association of Northern Minorities		
	Male	**Female**
1960s	62	62
1990s	45	55

Population figures for the Association of Northern Minorities			
	1950s	**1960s**	**1990s**
Percentage of total northern population	20	9	1.5

Total population: 183 700

D

Future of a people

Since the fall of Russian communism in the early 1990s there have been a number of changes which could benefit the Northern Minorities. These include:

- the setting up of an Association of Northern Minorities
- a return to ownership of some of their lands
- new stricter pollution controls
- the creation of several new environmental protection areas.

3 Compare the history of the Nenet before and after 1917.

4 a Use **Source C** to describe how the tundra environment has been affected by industrial development.
b Explain how this may have affected the lives of the Nenet.

5 Discuss the benefits to the Nenet of the measures described in 'Future of a people'.

6 Use **Source D** and other evidence to write a letter to the Russian government concerning its future treatment of the area.

2.8 Hearts of oak ... are no more

How have people exploited the resources of the deciduous forest ecosystem?

How will plants, animals and habitats be affected by further exploitation?

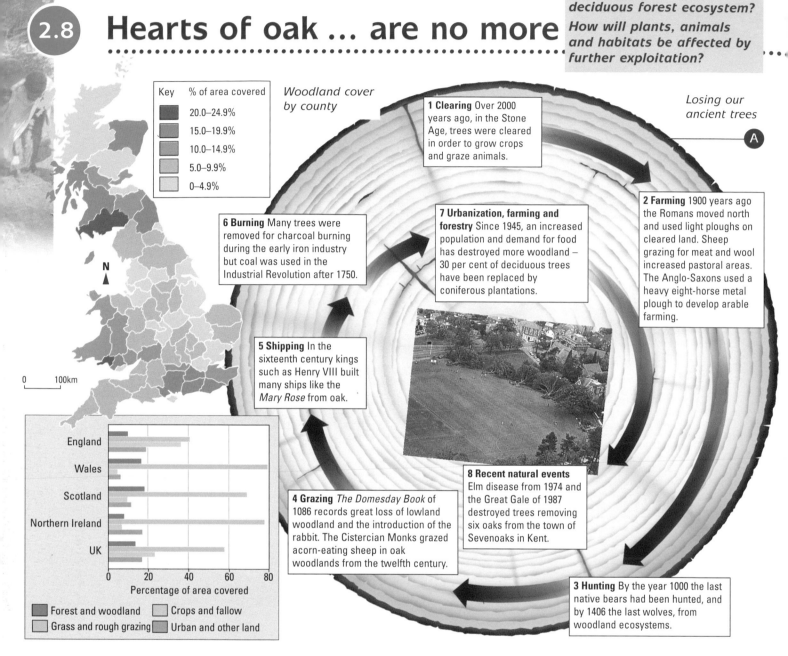

Key % of area covered
- 20.0–24.9%
- 15.0–19.9%
- 10.0–14.9%
- 5.0–9.9%
- 0–4.9%

Woodland cover by county

Losing our ancient trees

A

1 Clearing Over 2000 years ago, in the Stone Age, trees were cleared in order to grow crops and graze animals.

2 Farming 1900 years ago the Romans moved north and used light ploughs on cleared land. Sheep grazing for meat and wool increased pastoral areas. The Anglo-Saxons used a heavy eight-horse metal plough to develop arable farming.

6 Burning Many trees were removed for charcoal burning during the early iron industry but coal was used in the Industrial Revolution after 1750.

7 Urbanization, farming and forestry Since 1945, an increased population and demand for food has destroyed more woodland – 30 per cent of deciduous trees have been replaced by coniferous plantations.

5 Shipping In the sixteenth century kings such as Henry VIII built many ships like the *Mary Rose* from oak.

8 Recent natural events Elm disease from 1974 and the Great Gale of 1987 destroyed trees removing six oaks from the town of Sevenoaks in Kent.

4 Grazing *The Domesday Book* of 1086 records great loss of lowland woodland and the introduction of the rabbit. The Cistercian Monks grazed acorn-eating sheep in oak woodlands from the twelfth century.

3 Hunting By the year 1000 the last native bears had been hunted, and by 1406 the last wolves, from woodland ecosystems.

0   100km

England
Wales
Scotland
Northern Ireland
UK

0   20   40   60   80
Percentage of area covered

- Forest and woodland
- Crops and fallow
- Grass and rough grazing
- Urban and other land

Trees – a waste of space?

It is difficult to believe that around 2000 years ago trees dominated the British landscape. **Wildwood** forests stretched across the countryside and deciduous trees like oak, elm and beech were all common in the south. In the colder north, coniferous trees such as pines were dominant. Britain should naturally be covered in trees.

Human activity has removed much of the wildwood and very few ancient forests remain. Does this matter?

1 Study the information in **Source A**.
   a Draw a time-line showing the reasons for tree loss caused by human activities.
   b Which recent natural events have caused tree loss?

2 a Which animals have disappeared from deciduous ecosystems in the UK? Explain this loss.
   b How did the introduction of grazing animals cause tree loss?

3 What type of trees have been planted in place of native oak and beech forests since 1945? Suggest why this is happening.

4 Study the map and table in **Source A**.
   a Describe the distribution of wooded areas in the UK.
   b Use an atlas to suggest how climate, relief and altitude, and human activity may have influenced this distribution.

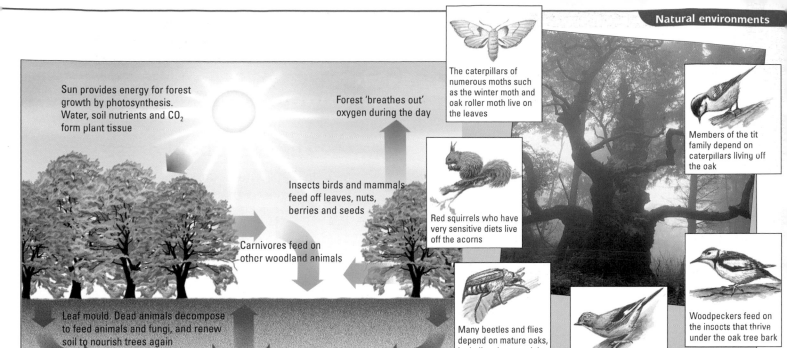

Sun provides energy for forest growth by photosynthesis. Water, soil nutrients and CO_2 form plant tissue

Forest 'breathes out' oxygen during the day

Insects birds and mammals feed off leaves, nuts, berries and seeds

Carnivores feed on other woodland animals

Leaf mould. Dead animals decompose to feed animals and fungi, and renew soil to nourish trees again

The caterpillars of numerous moths such as the winter moth and oak roller moth live on the leaves

Members of the tit family depend on caterpillars living off the oak

Red squirrels who have very sensitive diets live off the acorns

Many beetles and flies depend on mature oaks, including the rare violet click beetle

Birds such as jays and wood pigeons live off the acorns

Woodpeckers feed on the insects that thrive under the oak tree bark

B *The deciduous woodland ecosystem*

C *The Wye valley, Herefordshire*

NOW

THE FUTURE?

5 Study **Source B**.
a Draw a simple food chain showing links between a producer, primary consumer (herbivore) and secondary consumer (carnivore).
b What problems will the loss of oak trees cause for the wildlife shown?
c Suggest other problems caused by tree loss.

6 Look at **Source C**.
a What is the same in both pictures?
b Describe how the following will change:
  (i) woodland and hedgerows
  (ii) field size and shapes
  (iii) rural settlements
  (iv) traffic and communication links
  (v) location of industrial work.
c Explain how different groups of people would gain or lose from these changes.

2.9 Putting the trees back

Key
- Area of National Forest
- ⋯ Canal
- Main roads
- Motorways
- ❷ Areas where first trees planted

❶ Sarah's Wood
❷ Burton upon Trent
❸ Willesley Wood
❹ Trees planted along A50
❺ Snibston Discovery Park
❻ Martin's Wood
❼ Bardon Hill Quarry

The National Forest Ⓐ

The National Forest

In 1990 the Countryside Commission announced that the Midlands had been chosen as the site for a new National Forest.

The aim is to plant one third of the area with new woodland. The growth of heathland and meadows will be encouraged in clearings where trees cannot grow. The forest should help to bring prosperity back to a depressed region.

Why a National Forest?

- There is an increasing concern about the quality and appearance of Britain's disappearing countryside.
- There is a surge of interest in creating new woodlands for timber, recreation and pleasure.
- Trees are ecologically vital, keeping the mammal world breathing by taking in carbon dioxide and giving out oxygen.

Countryside Commission

Giant forest for the nation to be sown in coal-scarred Midlands

'This is a depressed area needing a lot of work', claimed a member of the Countryside Commission team. 'Industry has polluted the soil which can only be turned into heath-land. Farmers have removed old hedgerows creating open fields. We are now involving schools in planting trees which will bring jobs. These young people will be the foresters of tomorrow whereas their fathers were the miners of yesterday'.

One difficulty may be land ownership. There is no compulsory purchase so the National Forest Company must convince landowners that it is worth planting trees. The European Union (EU) will pay farmers to set aside land for tree planting instead of growing unwanted crops. Grants will be given to landowners who provide public access to woods.

The plan includes wildlife reserves, fishing ponds, a visitor centre and leisure pursuits such as cycling and orienteering within easy reach of 30 million people. There will also be an 8 megawatt power station fuelled by wood cut from willows and poplar. Forestry management courses will be available to support the timber industry. Conifer plantations will produce softwood, and high quality hardwood from oaks and cherries will be sold. These will be thinned out to allow the strongest trees to create a mature forest in the twenty-first century.

County	1949	1982	2001
Leicestershire	2.3	3	?
Derbyshire	4.1	5.1	?
Staffordshire	5.4	6.2	?
UK Average	5.8	7.1	

Figures in percentages
Source: Census of Woodland and Trees 1947–49 and 1979–82 FC

Ⓑ

Tree cover in the National Forest Counties

The next census of woodlands and trees will be carried out in 2001. We expect to see an increase in tree cover in the National Forest counties.

1 Study **Source A**.
a List the Countryside Commission's reasons for creating a new forest in the UK.
b Describe the area planned for the National Forest. Refer to: location; size; settlement; transport routes.
c Use **Source B** to help you explain the choice of the Midlands for the National Forest.

2 Read **Source C**.
a Why is this region described as 'depressed'?
b How is the National Forest Company and European Union (EU) trying to encourage landowners to plant more trees?
c What job opportunities will be created in the National Forest?
d Suggest why a variety of trees are being planted.

Forests for the community

1990 was a good year for trees. As well as choosing the site for the National Forest, the Countryside Commission and Forestry Commission launched the Community Forest initiative.

Main urban area	Community Forest
Sunderland and Newcastle	The Great North Forest
Middlesbrough	Cleve...
Liverpool	The...
Manchester	
London	
Swindon	
St Albans	
Bristol	
Milton Keynes	
Stafford	
Mansfield	
Rotherham and Sheffield	

Whitburn Colliery and Old Marsden

North of Sunderland is an area that will form part of the north-east edge of the Great North Forest. The wild coastline of limestone cliffs and stacks stands cheek by jowl with industry. Marsden Quarry and some preserved Lime Kilns are next to the top road. Built in the 1870s for burning lime with coal from Whitburn Colliery for agricultural fertilizer, they were in use until the 1960s.

Coal mining took place in the derelict area in the foreground. It is hoped this will become a prime site on the Heritage Coast. Souter Lighthouse, now in the hands of the National Trust, was built in 1871. It was equipped with a foghorn to warn ships of dangerous rocks. It stopped operating in 1988.

There was once a village here. Old Marsden had a short life: from about 1874, when the coal mine opened, to the 1950s, when the pits began to close. There were nine streets, 134 houses and a population of about 700. In dry summers the outline of the terraced housing can still be seen in the grass which has grown over the site.

The pit finally closed in 1968 and there is little on the ground now to show the route of the colliery railway. The church, school, Miners' Institute, shops, pits and railway have all vanished.

Where are the Community Forests?

D

E

Creating the Great North Community Forest

F

Community Forests: the aims
These forests are intended to cover large areas on the edge of town and cities. They will:

1. improve damaged environments e.g. old mine workings.
2. provide increased access to sport, recreation, and cultural events in a wooded landscape.
3. encourage high levels of community involvement and provide a resource for schools.
4. protect and create sites for nature conservation.
5. provide timber and timber-based industries and woodland products.

3 Study **Source D**.
   a Copy and complete the table.
   b Describe the location of the Great North Forest.
   c Describe Whitburn's location.

4 Study **Source E**.
   a List the past job opportunities that were provided by the natural resources here.
   b How has the environment here changed during the last fifty years?

5 The managers of the Great North Forest have invited schools to send in their ideas for developing the area in the photo.
   a Devise a development plan for the area. It must meet the Community Forest aims in **Source F**.
   b Fully justify your plan.

2.10 Mediterranean wetlands

How have natural events and human activities changed wetland ecosystems?

Which human activities are causing damage to Mediterranean wetland ecosystems?

A *Don't drink the water!*

Agricultural inputs: fertilizers and pesticides are sprayed on land by farmers; nutrients enrich the water and encourage algae growth.

Natural inputs: Water flowing over and under the ground washes mud and chemicals into the river. Rainfall is a weak carbonic acid which collects other chemicals as it falls.

Wetlands of the Po Delta, Italy

The end product of water pollution is usually water with more nutrients, toxic chemicals and acidity. This destroys fragile freshwater ecosystems. Algae thrive with more nutrients and use up all the oxygen in the water. Fish and other wetland wildlife suffocate. This process is called **eutrophication**.

Delta area

Industrial inputs: Chemical waste is discharged directly into the river from factories. Sulphur and nitrogen discharged into the air return as acid rain.

Other inputs: Ships and boats release diesel and petrol into the river water. Groundwater brings chemicals from land fill sites. Sewage farms release treated sewage into the water.

From sea: Oil rigs release oil into the sea which affects the delta as tides bring it in. Oil tankers can release surplus loads or run onto rocks causing oil spillages. Sewage outfalls can be returned to land further down the coast by longshore drift.

What is a wetland ecosystem?

Most of the ecosystems studied so far have evolved on land. Water plays a much greater role as an input to wetland ecosystems which are waterlogged areas. They vary in size from a wet, grassy corner of a small pond to huge **deltas** such as those at the ends of the Rhone, Nile and Po rivers in the Mediterranean.

Some of the most fragile ecosystems in the world are where freshwater meets saltwater. During the last two centuries human activity has changed wetland ecosystems. As Source **A** shows, a river can carry many different pollutants from a large drainage basin into estuaries and deltas where the river enters the sea.

1 Study **Source A**.
a Which natural inputs can pollute the river system?
b How can different types of human activity pollute the river system?
c Which activities may affect the delta area?
d How can the water and wildlife ecosystem be changed by pollution?

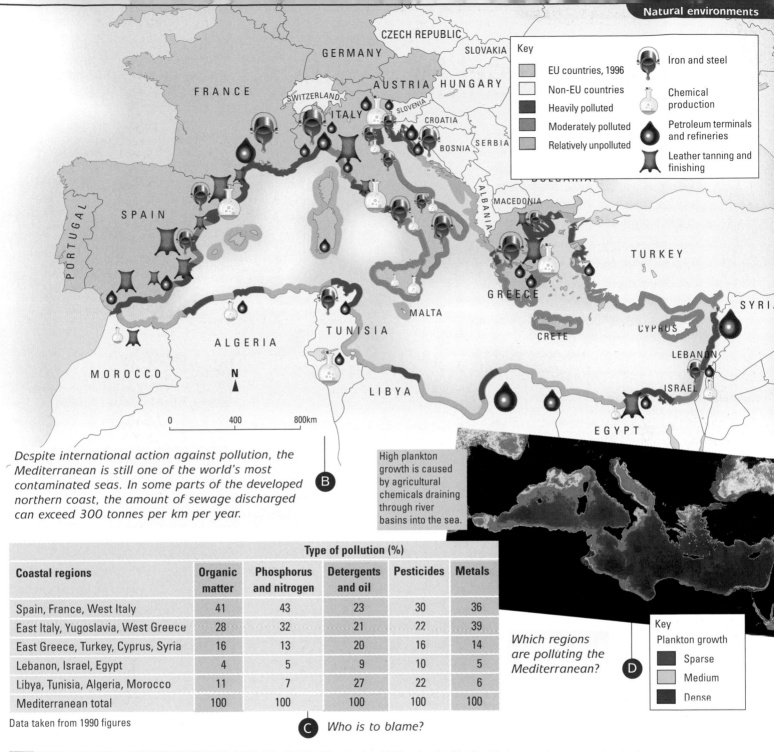

Key

EU countries, 1996
Non-EU countries
Heavily polluted
Moderately polluted
Relatively unpolluted

Iron and steel
Chemical production
Petroleum terminals and refineries
Leather tanning and finishing

Despite international action against pollution, the Mediterranean is still one of the world's most contaminated seas. In some parts of the developed northern coast, the amount of sewage discharged can exceed 300 tonnes per km per year.

B

High plankton growth is caused by agricultural chemicals draining through river basins into the sea.

Which regions are polluting the Mediterranean?

D

Key
Plankton growth

Sparse
Medium
Dense

Coastal regions	Type of pollution (%)				
	Organic matter	Phosphorus and nitrogen	Detergents and oil	Pesticides	Metals
Spain, France, West Italy	41	43	23	30	36
East Italy, Yugoslavia, West Greece	28	32	21	22	39
East Greece, Turkey, Cyprus, Syria	16	13	20	16	14
Lebanon, Israel, Egypt	4	5	9	10	5
Libya, Tunisia, Algeria, Morocco	11	7	27	22	6
Mediterranean total	100	100	100	100	100

Data taken from 1990 figures

C *Who is to blame?*

2 Study the map in **Source B**.
a Describe the distribution of pollution.
b Compare this with the location of industrial areas.
c Comment on your findings.

3 Study **Source C**.
a Draw graphs to represent this information.
b Which two coastal regions are responsible for most of the pollution?
c Which two coastal regions contribute least pollution?

4 Study **Source D**.
a Why is plankton growth a useful indicator of pollution?
b Use the satellite image to describe the distribution of pollution by agricultural chemicals.
c Use an atlas to name three deltas which are badly polluted.

5 'More Economically Developed Countries (MEDC) in the European Union (EU) are responsible for most of the pollution of Mediterranean wetlands.' Justify this statement.

2.11 The Delta del Po ... llution!

The delta

Deltas create a great variety of wetland ecosystems. Many are under threat as human activity makes increased demands on them.

The Rhone (Camargue), Nile and Po deltas have formed on the Mediterranean coasts. They each face similar problems. The Po Delta faces indirect threats from pollution and direct threats from development on the delta itself. Conflict is inevitable.

The wetlands are the most important Italian marshes for breeding water birds and for winter migrants. Over 350 species use sandbanks, humps and other wetland habitats.

River Po

Key
- ▨ Woods and pine plantations
- ▨ Beaches and sandbanks
- ▨ Wetlands

A The Po Delta and its plants and wildlife

Phosphorus pollution in the Po Delta

Other 7%
Fertilizers 18%
Urban and industrial waste 67%
Animal waste 13%

B The Po Delta needs protection from the North Italian Plain

Nitrogen pollution in the Po Delta

Fertilizers 26%
Urban and industrial waste 43%
Animal waste 8%
Other 23%

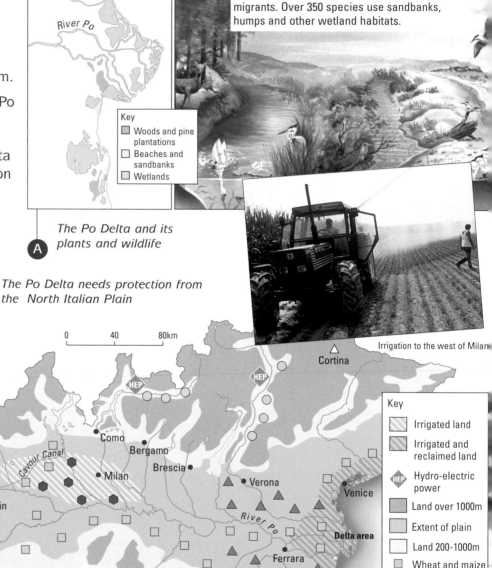

Irrigation to the west of Milan

Key
- ▨ Irrigated land
- ▨ Irrigated and reclaimed land
- ◆ HEP Hydro-electric power
- ▨ Land over 1000m
- ▨ Extent of plain
- ▢ Land 200–1000m
- ▢ Wheat and maize
- ▲ Rice
- ⬡ Orchards
- ○ Vines

0   40   80km

N

Mont Blanc
Como
Bergamo
Brescia
Milan
Verona
Turin
Venice
River Po
Delta area
Ferrara
Genoa
Bologna   Ravenna
Cavour Canal
Cortina

The River Po runs through Italy's most productive region. It picks up tonnes of waste from industrial use and agro-chemicals used in farming. Irrigation in the west produces the world's highest yields per hectare but extracts huge amounts of water from the Po. This means other parts of the Po can run dry. Sand and gravel are also extracted for building purposes. Closer to the delta the Po flows above its floodplain. Rapidly melting snow can cause flooding in the lower part of the valley.

1 Study **Source A**.
  a Which three different types of environment are shown on the map?
  b Explain why this area has such diverse wildlife.

2 Study **Source B**.
  a Describe the drainage pattern of the River Po from its sources to the delta.
  b List the main towns and cities the tributaries feeding the River Po pass through. Suggest how these may contribute to river pollution.
  c Which human activities have indirect and direct impacts along the river and its delta? Explain your answer.

Down on the Delta

Nature and human activity have co-existed for many years on the Po Delta. There are ten National Parks in Italy. The Po Delta may become another.

This will promote traditional activities such as hunting and clam fishing as well as allowing some development that is compatible with the environment.

C

The human impact on environmental systems of the Po Delta

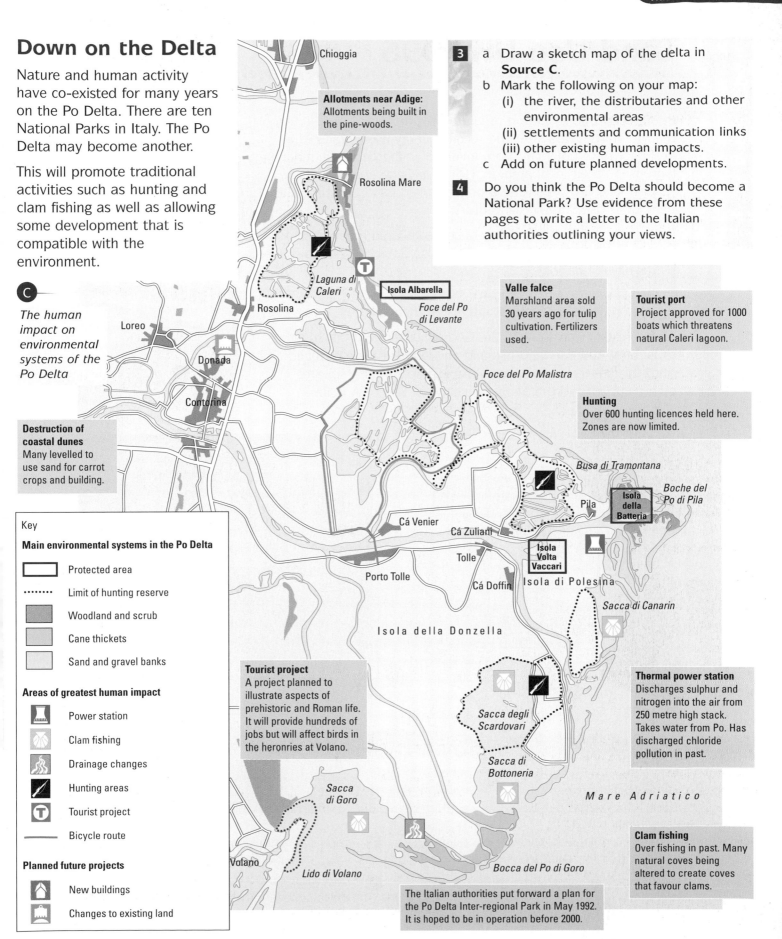

3 a Draw a sketch map of the delta in **Source C**.
  b Mark the following on your map:
   (i) the river, the distributaries and other environmental areas
   (ii) settlements and communication links
   (iii) other existing human impacts.
  c Add on future planned developments.

4 Do you think the Po Delta should become a National Park? Use evidence from these pages to write a letter to the Italian authorities outlining your views.

Allotments near Adige: Allotments being built in the pine-woods.

Valle falce Marshland area sold 30 years ago for tulip cultivation. Fertilizers used.

Tourist port Project approved for 1000 boats which threatens natural Caleri lagoon.

Hunting Over 600 hunting licences held here. Zones are now limited.

Destruction of coastal dunes Many levelled to use sand for carrot crops and building.

Tourist project A project planned to illustrate aspects of prehistoric and Roman life. It will provide hundreds of jobs but will affect birds in the heronries at Volano.

Thermal power station Discharges sulphur and nitrogen into the air from 250 metre high stack. Takes water from Po. Has discharged chloride pollution in past.

Clam fishing Over fishing in past. Many natural coves being altered to create coves that favour clams.

The Italian authorities put forward a plan for the Po Delta Inter-regional Park in May 1992. It is hoped to be in operation before 2000.

Key

Main environmental systems in the Po Delta

☐ Protected area
⋯⋯ Limit of hunting reserve
▨ Woodland and scrub
▨ Cane thickets
▨ Sand and gravel banks

Areas of greatest human impact

⌂ Power station
◉ Clam fishing
♨ Drainage changes
◪ Hunting areas
Ⓣ Tourist project
— Bicycle route

Planned future projects

⌂ New buildings
⌂ Changes to existing land

Labels on map: Chioggia, Rosolina Mare, Rosolina, Loreo, Donada, Contorina, Laguna di Caleri, Isola Albarella, Foce del Po di Levante, Foce del Po Malistra, Busa di Tramontana, Pila, Isola della Batteria, Boche del Po di Pila, Cá Venier, Cá Zuliani, Tolle, Isola Volta Vaccari, Porto Tolle, Cá Doffin, Isola di Polesina, Sacca di Canarin, Isola della Donzella, Sacca degli Scardovari, Sacca di Bottoneria, Mare Adriatico, Sacca di Goro, Volano, Lido di Volano, Bocca del Po di Goro

2 Land Use-UK 1996

In 1930 Dr Dudley Stamp organized the first Land Use Survey of the UK. Thirty years later the second survey was organized by Professor Alice Coleman. Both involved young people in mapping land-use in their local area. In 1996 the Geographical Association (GA) organized a project called Land Use-UK – the third Land Use Survey this century.

During the summer thousands of schoolchildren mapped the land use of a local grid square. They also noted down two other pieces of information:

1 changes in the last five years
2 environmental issues that interested them.

All the results were sent to the GA in Sheffield and put together to find out how the land-use and environment have changed since the previous two surveys. An example of grid squares before and after the mapping is shown in Source **A** below.

We're surveying for
land use UK
GEOGRAPHICAL ASSOCIATION
SHEFFIELD S10 3BP

Students from Finha Park school, COVENT

A *1996 land-use map of grid square 5697 (below) ... and one the Ordnance Survey did earlier*

Key
- Grass
- Woodland and shrubs
- Wetland and water
- Transport routes and features
- Residential
- Commercial and business uses
- Industrial premises
- Public institutions
- Tended open space
- Derelict and waste land and buildings
- Land in transition

Scale: 1:10 000 (10cm = 1km)

© Crown Copyright

1 Study the maps in **Source A**. Why do you think this scale map was used for 'Land Use-UK'?

2 Use evidence from the maps above to describe the land use in 1996.

3 Carry out a similar survey and map your local land-use. Compare it to the survey above.

4 Does your survey show any environmental issues which concern or interest you? What could you, your school and community do about them?

3

Issues of global concern

KEY IDEAS

Change in natural environments related to weather and climate may be of international concern.

Greenpeace members investigate ice melt in Antarctica, February 1997

53

3.1 Wind and acid rain

How is acid rain created?
How are the effects of acid rain spread?

What is acid rain?

People's activities pollute much of the world's air. Pollution can occur in many ways but often involves burning materials as a source of power. Burning fossil fuels like coal, oil and natural gas releases sulphur dioxide and nitrogen oxides. These gases usually escape into the atmosphere and dissolve in the water droplets of clouds. In this way atmospheric pollution becomes incorporated into the water cycle and the result is acid precipitation.

The wind, however, can carry polluted water droplets for great distances before they fall as rain or snow. So acid rain can affect people and environments far removed from the area where the pollution originally formed.

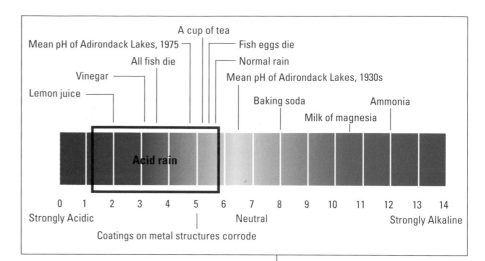

The range of pH values that relate to a number of common materials, showing the level for acid rain

A

Thermal power station at Middleburg in eastern Pennsylvania, USA

B

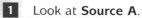

1 Look at **Source A**.
  a List three materials which are acidic and three which are alkaline.
  b What is the pH of normal rain?
  c What is the pH of the most damaging acid rain?

2 Study **Source B**.
  a Label a sketch of the thermal power station with the following: cooling towers, chimneys, conveyor belt.
  b Based on this evidence suggest and label location for the coalstore and the power house.
  c Label the main points at which polluting gasses enter the atmoshere.
  d Add a brief sentence to each of your labels to explain what is happening at each place.
  e Suggest a relationship between chimney height and the distance pollution travels. Explain your answers.

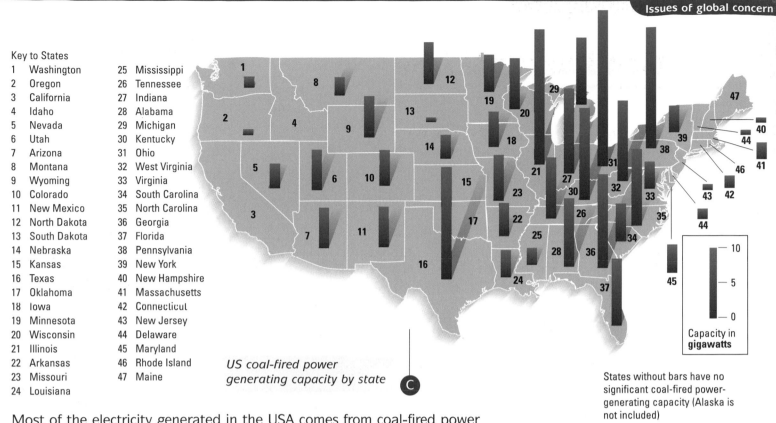

Key to States

1	Washington	25	Mississippi
2	Oregon	26	Tennessee
3	California	27	Indiana
4	Idaho	28	Alabama
5	Nevada	29	Michigan
6	Utah	30	Kentucky
7	Arizona	31	Ohio
8	Montana	32	West Virginia
9	Wyoming	33	Virginia
10	Colorado	34	South Carolina
11	New Mexico	35	North Carolina
12	North Dakota	36	Georgia
13	South Dakota	37	Florida
14	Nebraska	38	Pennsylvania
15	Kansas	39	New York
16	Texas	40	New Hampshire
17	Oklahoma	41	Massachusetts
18	Iowa	42	Connecticut
19	Minnesota	43	New Jersey
20	Wisconsin	44	Delaware
21	Illinois	45	Maryland
22	Arkansas	46	Rhode Island
23	Missouri	47	Maine
24	Louisiana		

Capacity in **gigawatts**

US coal-fired power generating capacity by state **C**

States without bars have no significant coal-fired power-generating capacity (Alaska is not included)

Most of the electricity generated in the USA comes from coal-fired power stations. As much as 85 per cent of all the coal mined in the USA is burned in these power stations. There is great concern about the pollution this creates and the impact it has on the immediate locality and on areas far away. Other sources of atmospheric pollution come from major urban areas and from centres of industry.

In the USA, the problems caused by the creation of acid rain cross state boundaries and also affect Canada. In other parts of the world, in Europe for example, many countries can be affected by the activities of one nation.

3 Using **Source C**, describe the distribution of coal-fired power stations in the USA.

4 Compare **Sources C** and **D**.
a What similarities and differences are there between the two maps?
b Suggest how the following help to explain your answer to 4a:
(i) the prevailing wind
(ii) sources of pollution other than thermal power stations.
c How are the Adirondack mountains affected by acid rain.

5 a Suggest which groups of people may be concerned about the effects of acid rain. Explain your answer.
b You are asked by your electricity company whether or not you would be prepared to pay an extra 10 per cent on your fuel bill to help reduce acid rain. Write a letter to the company to explain your position.

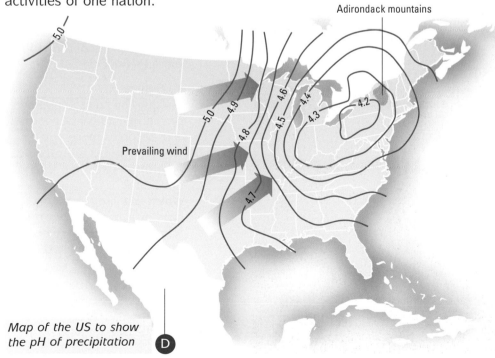

Adirondack mountains

Prevailing wind

Map of the US to show the pH of precipitation **D**

3.2 Acidified lakes

An acidified lake in the Adirondack Mountains of New York State, USA. Almost 6 per cent of all the ponds and lakes of this area are badly affected by acid rain: from the mid-1930s to the mid-1970s the pH of the Adirondack lakes changed from 5.5 to 4.5

Evenings I often stroll out on my cabin deck to enjoy the view of an Adirondack lake. But the scene is not as I remember it. No trout rise to the water's surface, swirling sunset colours. No ospreys quest along the shoreline, scanning for fish. No otters sprawl on my rocky point, crunching bullheads [fish] for dinner. North and south of where I live are at least 180 fishless ponds.

Fishermen on a lake in the Adirondacks

What can be done?

Since 1970 there have been several **Clean Air Acts** to reduce the problem of sulphur emission in the United States. Power stations were given until the year 2000 to halve their sulphur output. Although this would improve areas like the Adirondacks, it could cause the loss of 14 000 jobs in the eastern coalfields of the USA. They would be replaced by about 17 000 new jobs in the west of the country. Here there is cleaner coal which has a lower sulphur content.

1 Look at **Source A**.
  a How can you tell that the area has suffered from the effects of acid rain?
  b What evidence is there that this is a serious problem for the Adirondack area?

2 Study **Source B**.
  a Which living creature would be the first to die out as the lake becomes more acid?
  b Which creatures are capable of withstanding high levels of acidity?
  c Which lake life forms would have disappeared from the Adirondack lakes between the mid-1930s and mid-1970s?

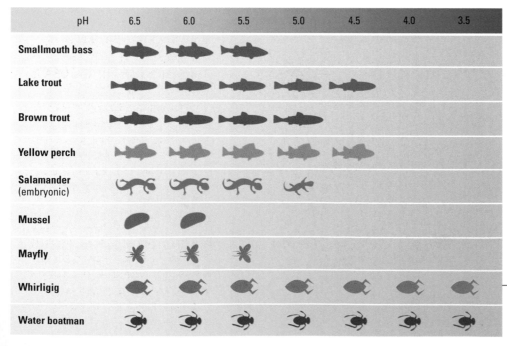

pH	6.5	6.0	5.5	5.0	4.5	4.0	3.5
Smallmouth bass	✓	✓	✓				
Lake trout	✓	✓	✓	✓	✓		
Brown trout	✓	✓	✓	✓			
Yellow perch	✓	✓	✓	✓	✓		
Salamander (embryonic)	✓	✓	✓	✓			
Mussel	✓	✓					
Mayfly	✓	✓	✓				
Whirligig	✓	✓	✓	✓	✓	✓	✓
Water boatman	✓	✓	✓	✓	✓	✓	✓

The effects of pH values on life in the Adirondack lakes

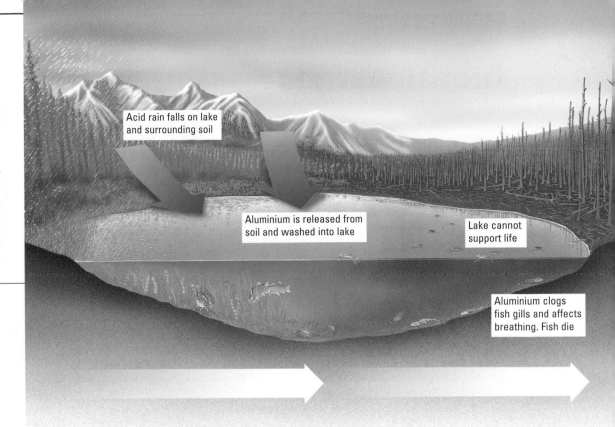

It snows a lot in the Adirondacks. Fish spawn in spring just when the acid snow melts. The young fry [fish] can't take the shock of the run-off; eventually the lake becomes empty. Many of these eastern lakes can't support any life at all.

C

Acid rain falls on lake and surrounding soil

Aluminium is released from soil and washed into lake

Lake cannot support life

Aluminium clogs fish gills and affects breathing. Fish die

NUCLEAR PLANT LEAKS

Further along the road, at the village of Novoye Sharno, the radiation detector bleeps for the first time. 'Pay attention, please,' says Michael. 'The radiation is very high here.' This is one of the villages evacuated in 1986, immediately after the explosion and fire, and the village shop is almost submerged in undergrowth. Inside it is a mess of broken shelves, abandoned goods, smashed bottles. 'There was a panic here,' Vadim explains, unnecessarily.

Michael Palin, *Pole to Pole*, BBC Books (1992)

Alternatives to burning fossil fuels: Nuclear power, solar power, wind power and hydro-electric power

D

3
a Using **Source C**, describe how fish are affected by acid rain.
b Using evidence from these pages, describe the effects of acid rain on the food chain.

4 Pollution which leads to acid rain can be reduced by burning 'cleaner' coal.
a Suggest what is meant by 'cleaner' coal.
b In which parts of the USA is this coal found?
c How would its use affect employment opportunities?
d Discuss the view that 'job losses in one area of the USA are a price worth paying to improve the environment in another'.

5 Rather than burning fossil fuels, **Source D** shows some alternative ways to produce electricity. Investigate one of these fully and outline the advantages and disadvantages of using it for the environment.

3.3 Global warming – is it new?

Is temperature change new?
How do we know global temperatures are rising?
How has human activity contributed to global temperature rises?

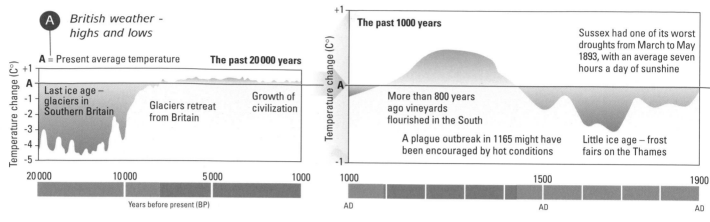

A British weather – highs and lows

A = Present average temperature

The past 20 000 years

Temperature change (C°)

Last ice age – glaciers in Southern Britain

Glaciers retreat from Britain

Growth of civilization

Years before present (BP)

The past 1000 years

Sussex had one of its worst droughts from March to May 1893, with an average seven hours a day of sunshine

More than 800 years ago vineyards flourished in the South

A plague outbreak in 1165 might have been encouraged by hot conditions

Little ice age – frost fairs on the Thames

Temperature changes are not new

Human activity is often blamed for global warming but it is not new. The Earth is over 4600 million years old. In that time it has been warmer with dry periods and cooler with ice sheets covering continents. These changes have taken place quite naturally without the influence of human activity.

What has caused concern in recent years have been the unusual weather and climate events reported in the media. Droughts, floods and hurricanes have affected places that are not used to such extreme weather.

Some of these changes are thought to be due to the activities of people rather than to nature alone.

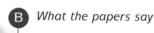

B *What the papers say*

Antarctic ice sheets melt as temperatures rise

Fears of global warming have been confirmed by the British Antarctic Survey as ice sheets begin to melt at an alarming rate. An area of ice the size of London has melted since 1950. In this time temperatures have risen by 2.5 C mostly due to pollution. The rapid melt is causing giant icebergs to break off causing hazards to shipping. For penguins and seals however this is good news. They will benefit by more rocky shores being exposed increasing habitats and sources of food supply.

Sea level rise puts deltas and islands at risk

Temperature increase gives Arctic trees early start to season

Spruce trees on the edge of the Arctic circle are sprouting early. Pollen is being produced in mid-March as the tundra region moves northward. Scientists noted that twenty years ago these trees were dormant at the start of spring. There were no cones or pollen being produced. Now they are all ready for the advance north as the spring and summer seasons warm up and melt the frozen surface. Global warming means the tree-line will move further north in Canada and Siberia.

Atlantic fishing grounds show increase in warm water fish

1 Study **Source A**.
  a Describe the general trend in temperature change in the past 20,000 years.
  b Describe the changes in temperature between AD 1000 and AD 1900.
  c There was less concern about temperature change at the start of the twentieth century than there is at its end. To what extent does the graph support this concern?
  d Complete a table like the one opposite to show the effects of temperature change in Britain.

2 Read the articles in **Source B**.
  a What is happening to global temperature?
  b Describe the evidence for this change from:
  i) the Antarctic   ii) the Arctic   iii) the Atlantic Ocean.

Date	Warmer or colder than present average temperature?	Effects
20 000 BP	Colder	Ice Age
8000 – 5000 BP		

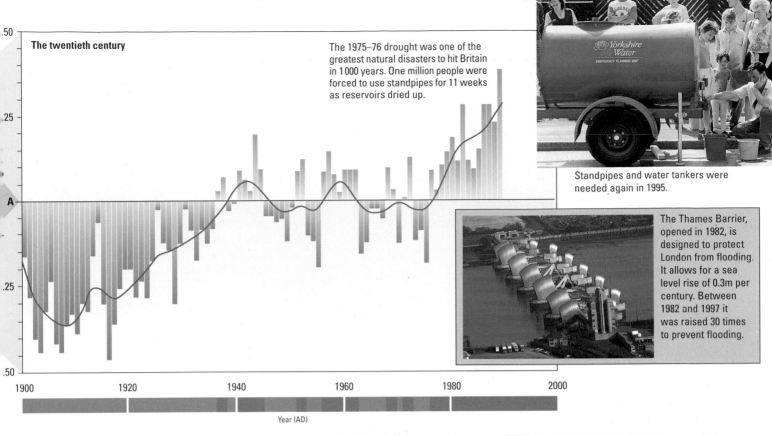

The twentieth century

.50

.25

A

.25

.50

The 1975–76 drought was one of the greatest natural disasters to hit Britain in 1000 years. One million people were forced to use standpipes for 11 weeks as reservoirs dried up.

Standpipes and water tankers were needed again in 1995.

The Thames Barrier, opened in 1982, is designed to protect London from flooding. It allows for a sea level rise of 0.3m per century. Between 1982 and 1997 it was raised 30 times to prevent flooding.

1900   1920   1940   1960   1980   2000

Year (AD)

Source C shows some ways in which human activity is adding to what may be a natural warm period. The main problem is the amount of carbon we are adding to, or leaving in the atmosphere. We need to be concerned about this because all life on the planet is carbon-based.

Too much carbon in the atmosphere means more heat from the earth's surface can be trapped. Greenhouse gases that trap heat include methane, water vapour, chloro-fluoro-carbons (CFCs) and nitrogen oxides. An increase in any of these can cause global temperatures to rise.

3 Study **Source C**.
a Why is this process called the greenhouse effect?
b What impact on global temperatures could the following have:
 (i) destroying rainforest in tropical regions
 (ii) burning fossil fuels like coal, gas and oil in factories
 (iii) banning the use of aerosols and fridge-freezers
 (iv) decreasing the number of motor vehicles using fossil fuels?
Justify your answers.

c What role do the oceans play in reducing carbon in the atmosphere? How might this change if temperatures rise?

4 'There is nothing people can do to reduce the increase in global temperatures.'

Do you agree with this statement? Use evidence from these pages to support your views.

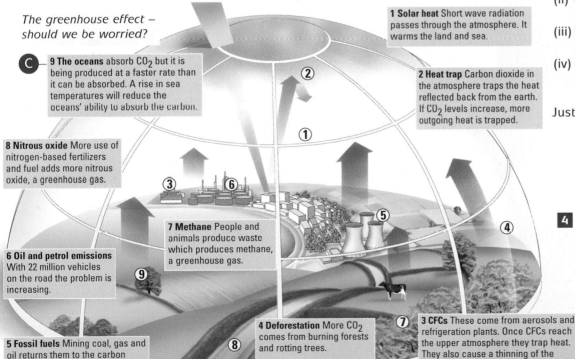

The greenhouse effect – should we be worried?

C

1 Solar heat Short wave radiation passes through the atmosphere. It warms the land and sea.

2 Heat trap Carbon dioxide in the atmosphere traps the heat reflected back from the earth. If CO_2 levels increase, more outgoing heat is trapped.

9 The oceans absorb CO_2 but it is being produced at a faster rate than it can be absorbed. A rise in sea temperatures will reduce the oceans' ability to absorb the carbon.

8 Nitrous oxide More use of nitrogen-based fertilizers and fuel adds more nitrous oxide, a greenhouse gas.

7 Methane People and animals produce waste which produces methane, a greenhouse gas.

6 Oil and petrol emissions With 22 million vehicles on the road the problem is increasing.

5 Fossil fuels Mining coal, gas and oil returns them to the carbon cycle. Burning these fuels adds more carbon to the atmosphere.

4 Deforestation More CO_2 comes from burning forests and rotting trees.

3 CFCs These come from aerosols and refrigeration plants. Once CFCs reach the upper atmosphere they trap heat. They also cause a thinning of the protective ozone layer, allowing more ultra-violet rays into the atmosphere.

3.4 If nothing is done about global warming...

One of the consequences of global warming is that ice sheets will melt and the world's sea level will rise. This will not only flood low-lying coastal areas but also deltas and islands.

Country	Total emissions (million metric tonnes)	Emissions per person (tonnes)
USA	1,392	5.35
China	848	0.76
Russia	462	3.22
Japan	303	2.53
Germany	237	2.96
India	225	0.31
United Kingdom	155	2.69
Ukraine	127	2.47
Canada	118	4.01
Italy	106	1.86

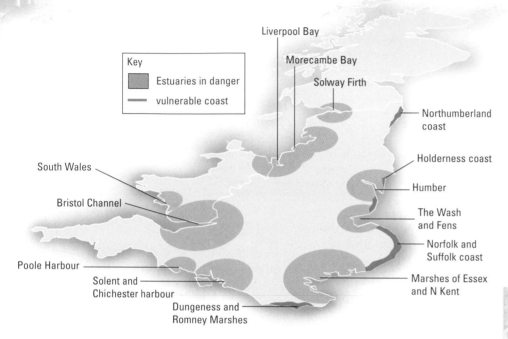

Key
Estuaries in danger
vulnerable coast

Liverpool Bay
Morecambe Bay
Solway Firth
Northumberland coast
Holderness coast
Humber
The Wash and Fens
Norfolk and Suffolk coast
Marshes of Essex and N Kent
Dungeness and Romney Marshes
Solent and Chichester harbour
Poole Harbour
Bristol Channel
South Wales

Gains and losses in England and Wales

B

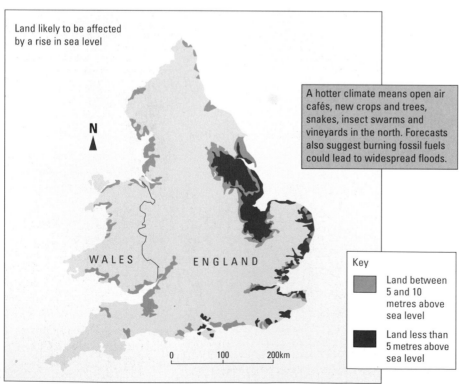

Land likely to be affected by a rise in sea level

A hotter climate means open air cafés, new crops and trees, snakes, insect swarms and vineyards in the north. Forecasts also suggest burning fossil fuels could lead to widespread floods.

N

WALES   ENGLAND

Key
Land between 5 and 10 metres above sea level
Land less than 5 metres above sea level

0   100   200km

1 Much of the global warming is caused by an increase in carbon dioxide levels in the atmosphere.
a Use **Source A** to draw a bar graph showing the total emissions produced by each country.
b Shade in the bars of those countries that you consider to be MEDCs and LEDCs.
c On your graph rank the countries from 1 (most carbon emitted per person) to 10 (least carbon emitted per person).
d Comment on your findings.
e Some LEDCs are trying to improve their economies by developing manufacturing industry. How may this affect future temperature changes? What are your views on this?

2 Study **Source B**.
a Describe the distribution of areas under threat from sea-level rise.
b How might these changes affect where you live or visit?

Who will gain and lose from global warming?
What is being done about global warming?

The time to act is now!

Global warming is now an international issue of concern. Governments in both MEDCs and LEDCs are aware that they must act quickly to protect the environment. There have been several conferences to discuss what could be done. Although some agreements have been made, these will not always reduce the problem as quickly as some countries want. This particularly applies to areas with low-lying deltas like the one in Bangladesh, and small islands like the Carteret Islands in the Solomon Sea. Their altitude is so low that sea-level rise could see them disappear in the twenty-first century.

3 Study **Source C**.
a List the agreements made at Berlin in 1995.
b Why were the Carteret Islanders disappointed with the Berlin conference?
c Do you agree with the AOSIS spokesperson? Explain your answer.

4 As an AOSIS representative, you have been invited to speak at the next Climate Conference. Your audience will include politicians from MEDCs.
a Collect information on an island of your choice from **Source D**.
b Produce a labelled map showing the main features and attractions. This will form part of your presentation.
c Prepare a short speech outlining your views on the impact of global warming on your island.

The conference has agreed that
1 Existing commitments of MEDCs to curb greenhouse gases are not adequate.
2 The developed countries now promise to reduce carbon levels to that of 1990 by the year 2000.
3 Target figures for 2005, 2010 and 2020 be set down.
4 All LEDCs should record all carbon emissions. They need not reduce these emissions yet.
The conference rejects an AOSIS plea that MEDCs cut carbon dioxide emissions to 20% below 1990 levels by the year 2000. They will find it difficult enough to reach the 1990 targets by then!

A spokesperson for the Association of Small Island States (AOSIS) said, 'We are very disappointed with the recent climate conference. We need a quicker reduction than the MEDCs are willing to attempt. If they lived where I do on the Carteret Islands, they would think differently. Recently a tidal wave washed away soils and the 1700 people there needed emergency rice supplies. The sea level has risen by 30cm a year since 1991 and three times a year we have nearly been submerged. If nothing is done, nobody will be able to live here within five years. We will have to move to other islands losing our homes, jobs and culture. Do these people care? We suspect not.'

Press release from Berlin Conference 1995

C *Meetings... and conferences... and summits...*

Some of the 36 Alliance of Small Island States (AOSIS) are so low-lying that they, plus the Ganges and Nile deltas in Bangladesh and Egypt, could be inundated in the next century by a rise in sea level.

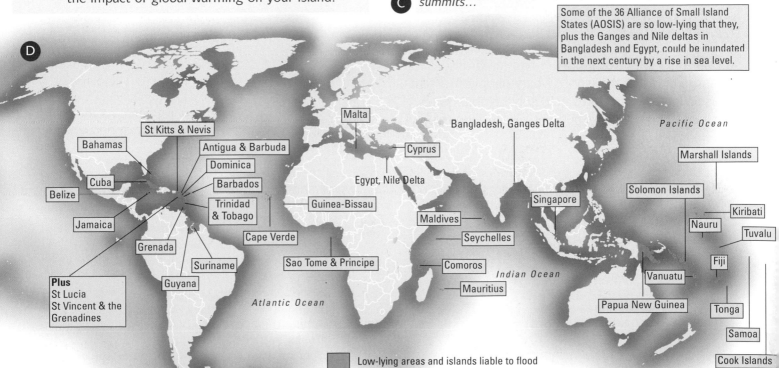

Malta
St Kitts & Nevis
Bahamas
Antigua & Barbuda
Dominica
Cuba
Barbados
Belize
Cyprus
Egypt, Nile Delta
Bangladesh, Ganges Delta
Pacific Ocean
Marshall Islands
Solomon Islands
Trinidad & Tobago
Guinea-Bissau
Jamaica
Singapore
Kiribati
Nauru
Maldives
Tuvalu
Grenada
Cape Verde
Seychelles
Suriname
Sao Tome & Principe
Comoros
Indian Ocean
Fiji
Vanuatu
Guyana
Mauritius
Papua New Guinea
Tonga
Plus St Lucia St Vincent & the Grenadines
Atlantic Ocean
Samoa
Cook Islands

Low-lying areas and islands liable to flood

3 Don't just sit there...

SAY SOMETHING!

RSPB

GREENPEACE

WWF ©

the woodland trust ©

Protesters in treetop battle with bailiffs over M65 extension

Let it not be said and said unto your shame That there was beauty here before you came.

Opponents block scheme for £170 million runway at Manchester airport

Dorney residents oppose Eton's Olympic rowing lake

Victory for Save Oxleas Wood campaigners

People can protest...
In the UK people have the right to express their concern through various means of peaceful protest.

People can contribute...
Teenage volunteers cleaning a pond, Glasgow.

DO SOMETHING!

Acid rain and global warming are two major issues that affect large areas of the world. Many people feel that there is little they can do to help solve global issues, but you can make a contribution to improving the environment in your own area.

1 Look at the opening photo of Section 3 on page 53.
  a Find out about the Greenpeace organization.
  b Why do you think Greenpeace are concerned about the melting of the Antarctic ice sheet?

2 a What environmental issues are the organizations shown on the badges concerned about?
  b List some other groups that are involved in conservation:
    (i) in your local area
    (ii) at the national and global scale.

3 List the different types of UK issues that people are protesting about in **Source A**. Are you aware of any of these? If so, how did you find out about them?

4 a Identify one environmental issue that is causing concern in your local area.
  b Carry out research through the media, questionnaires or by visiting the area.
  c Describe any changes this issue will cause to people and the environment.
  d Outline the arguments being used by people or groups involved.
  e What could you do to influence the outcome?

Glossary

· ·

Accumulated rainfall — Rainfall totals in which a new day's total rainfall is added to that of previous days. *11*

Anticyclone — A high pressure weather system. Average sea-level pressure at the centre of the system is usually above 1000 millibars. *16*

Arid — Dry desert environments, hot or cold, where there is little, if any, rainfall causing a shortage of water. *12*

Beaufort Scale — A scale of wind speed ranging from 0 (Calm) to 12 (Hurricane). A figure of 12 is over 117 kmph (73 mph). *23*

Biomes — Large ecosystems at the global scale where the climate and vegetation is uniform. Human activity may have destroyed or changed parts of the biome. *32*

Biosphere — The regions of the earth and atmosphere where plants and animals live. *31*

Biosphere reserve — An ecosystem which is being protected from exploitation by government strategies. *39*

Clean Air Acts — Laws passed by national and state governments to control the burning of fossil fuels in homes and by industry. *56*

Climate — The average of weather conditions over a long period, at least thirty years. Temperature and precipitation are the most often used climate data and are shown on climate graphs. *7*

Cold front — The boundary where a cold air mass from the north meets and pushes into a warm air mass from the south. This is usually found in the mid-latitudes of the northern hemisphere as part of a depression. *20*

Continentality — Areas away from the sea do not have its cooling influence in summer nor its warming influence in winter. Consequently these continental areas have high annual temperature ranges.(see Maritime) *9*

Delta — A landform, often triangular in shape, that develops where a river meets a slow body of water such as a lake or ocean. Deposition of sediment eventually builds up above the water level forcing the river to split into distributaries forming a delta. *48*

Depression — A low-pressure weather system found in the mid-latitudes of the northern hemisphere where a tropical warm air mass pushes into an arctic cold air mass. Warm air rises to give low pressure at the centre of the weather system. This is usually less than 1000 millibars. *20*

Desert — A dry area, hot or cold, where total annual precipitation is less than 250 millimetres. Deserts are usually treeless due to lack of water. *33*

Ecosystem — A system of links between plants and animals (the living community) and the habitats where they live, including the non-living environment. *31*

Eutrophication — The process whereby an increase in nutrients in a body of water such as a lake or slow-moving river causes an increase in algae which uses up all the oxygen. This causes other vegetation and wildlife to die. *48*

Gley — A soil which is intermittently waterlogged in its lower horizons. The gleyed horizons are usually blue-grey. *40*

Gigawatt — A measure of capacity of power stations; the larger the gigawatt the greater the output. 1 gigawatt = 1000 million watts. *55*

Heat island — The building of towns and cities can change local weather by causing a build up of temperature in and above them. These temperatures are often higher than surrounding countryside and form a heat island. *26*

Hectare — A metric measure of area. 1 hectare = 100 x 100 metres = 2.47 acres *35*

Humus — Decomposed organic material from dead plants and animals that forms the top layer or horizon of a soil and gives a brown colour to the soil e.g. in a brown earth soil. *36*

Inorganic — Material that has never lived but contributes vital elements to life and the survival of ecosystems e.g. minerals from rocks. *31*

LEDC — Less economically developed countries *33*

Leaching — A chemical reaction which results in nutrients in the soil being replaced by hydrogen from rainfall. Nutrients are lost or move deeper down the profile. *36*

Lichen — A group of plants, fungus and algae, which are capable of growing on and colouring rocks, tree trunks, roofs and walls. Their roots and the chemicals they produce weather the rock surface to produce a thin soil. *40*

Local climate — Small-scale climates due to the influence of local land-use which are specific to particular areas, e.g. a school, forest, urban area, park. *28*

MEDC — More economically developed countries. *15*

Maritime — Areas close to or on the coast have their climate influenced by the sea. Due to differential heating the sea is cooler than the land in summer and warmer in winter. Consequently maritime climates do not have such large annual temperature ranges as found in continental climates. 7

Maximum temperature — The highest temperature recorded during a time period. This is usually during a 24 hour period but can be monthly or yearly. 17

Minimum temperature — The lowest temperature recorded during a time period. This is usually during a 24 hour period but can be monthly or yearly. 17

Monsoon — Derived from the arabic word *mawsim* meaning fixed season it is a seasonal change of wind direction. The monsoon refers to both dry and wet seasons although its common use refers to the wet season only. 12

Moss — Small plants which thrive in open damp conditions. They often succeed lichen in a plant succession. 40

Northern minorities people — An official grouping of the native peoples of the far north of the Russian Federation. 42

Nutrients — Materials which plants use for food. 36

Occluded front — The area close to the centre of a depression where the more rapidly moving cold front has caught up and undercut the warm front at the surface. Very heavy rainfall is caused by the warm air being forced to rise. 21

Organic — Material that is living, or once formed part of, a living plant or animal. 31

Permafrost — Permanently frozen ground that forms part of the tundra biome. Its top layer may melt in the short warm season to allow water to be available for plants and animals at the surface. 40

Photosynthesis — The process whereby plants take in the sun's energy with carbon dioxide and water to produce energy, oxygen and plant tissue. 45

Plankton — Drifting or floating organic life found at various depths in seas, lakes or rivers. 49

Radiation — Short-wave radiation is the energy given out by the sun. It penetrates the atmosphere and heats the earth's surface. The earth, being cooler than the sun, sends out long-wave radiation This can be trapped by the atmosphere so causing the greenhouse effect. 13

Rattan — Climbing plants with long thin stems which can be bent or woven. 39

Regeneration — Growing back again. 38

Resettlement site — An area to which people are forcibly moved by a government to make way for an alternative use of the land on which the people had previously lived. 39

Sago — A rich powdered starchy grain made from the soft centre of the stem of palm trees. It is the staple diet in many parts of the world. 37

State farms — Farms run by the government in the Russian Federation when it was a communist country and part of the Soviet Union. 43

Stewards — People entrusted with the management of property, including the environment, to ensure it is useful to future generations. 30

Subsistence — A means of supporting life by only being able to meet basic needs of food, water, and shelter. 15

Sustainable — Capable, by careful use and management, of being maintained for future generations. 30

Synoptic chart — A map which gives the general view of the weather over a large area for a short period of time. 16

Taiga — The biome that contains the northern coniferous forests of Europe, North America and Asia. 40

Temperate — Areas in the northern and southern hemispheres which do not experience great extremes of heat or cold. They are in the mid-latitudes between the hot Tropics and cold Polar regions. 7

Tropopause — The upper limit or ceiling of the atmosphere about 12 km above the earth's surface. Rising air meeting the tropopause is forced to move north or south towards the Poles or towards the Equator. 18

Tundra — The biome in northern Canada, northern Europe and Asia where the ground is permanently frozen for most of the year. Mostly treeless, lichen, moss, grasses and dwarf shrubs can grow here. 40

Warm front — The boundary between a warm tropical air mass and the cold arctic air mass. The warm air is forced to rise giving a low-pressure at the surface forming a depression in the mid-latitudes of the northern hemisphere. 20

Weather — Short-term day to day changes in the atmosphere. Weather recording usually includes rainfall, temperature, cloud cover, wind speed and direction. 6

Weathering — The breakdown of rock surfaces into smaller particles by the action of weather, plants and animals. Weathering takes place on the spot. It does not involve large-scale removal of material. 36

Wildwood — The original ancient woodland that covered the United Kingdom before human activity began to affect it. 44